# MALAYSIAN NATURE HANDBOOKS

## *General Editor*

### M. W. F. TWEEDIE

THE aim of the Malaysian Nature Handbooks is to provide a series of handy, well-illustrated guides to the fauna and flora of Malaysia and Singapore. They can, of course, be no more than introductory; the animal and plant life of Malaysia is on such a lavish scale that comprehensive accounts of the groups described in each of the Handbooks must be either severely technical or voluminous and correspondingly costly. The selection of species described in each one has been carefully made, however, to illustrate those most likely to be the first encountered by reasonably observant people residing in or visiting Malaysia and Singapore; reference to rarities or species confined to inaccessible country has been avoided, except where such species are of special interest.

It is the Editor's belief that interest in animals and plants is best aroused by providing the means of identifying and naming them. The emphasis of the Handbooks is therefore firstly on identification, but as much information on habits and biology is included as space will allow. It is hoped that they may be of use to schools in supplementing courses in nature study and biology, and a source of pleasure to that quite numerous assemblage of people whose complaint has been that they would gladly be naturalists if someone would show them the way.

OTHER TITLES IN THE SERIES

MALAYSIAN NATURE HANDBOOKS

# Common Birds of the Malay Peninsula

BY

## M. W. F. TWEEDIE

*Formerly Director of The Raffles Museum, Singapore*

**ILLUSTRATED BY A. FRASER-BRUNNER**

LONGMAN

LONGMAN MALAYSIA SDN. BHD.
3, Jalan Kilang A, 46050 Petaling Jaya,
Selangor Darul Ehsan.
Tel: 03-7920466, 7920803

*Associated companies, branches and representatives*
*throughout the world*

*First published 1960 under title COMMON MALAYAN BIRDS*
*Second edition 1970*
*New impression †1979*
*Reprinted †1983, 1989*

ISBN 0 582 69450 7

Common Birds of the Malay Peninsula

Printed by Art Printing Works Sdn. Bhd., Kuala Lumpur, Selangor Darul Ehsan.

# CONTENTS

vi

# LIST OF PLATES

WHERE THE SEX SYMBOLS ♂ (MALE) AND ♀ (FEMALE) ARE
NOT SHOWN THE BIRDS ILLUSTRATED ARE MALE

# INTRODUCTION TO SECOND EDITION

THE total number of species of birds recorded from the Malay Peninsula[1] is 603. In this book space is available to mention only about one quarter of them; but it must be remembered that the natural condition of this country, from which it has only recently emerged, is to be covered almost entirely, from the mountain peaks to the sea-shore, with thick forest. It follows that the natural habitat of very many of our birds will be primaeval forest or jungle. They live either in the continuous leafy canopy of the tree-tops or in undergrowth on the jungle floor, and are difficult to find and seldom seen.

Also a good proportion of our records is based on rare migrants and so-called vagrants, birds which occasionally stray to this country on their migratory wanderings, but are not regular visitors. All these are, from the point of view of the ordinary observer, rare birds. The remainder, which can be seen commonly in gardens and inhabited country, by the sea-shore, in the accessible fringe of the forest and by roads and paths in the hill stations, comprise certainly less than half of the total, and it is hoped that the selection made here will provide for identification of most of them.

Mention has been made of migratory birds. Practically all our birds in this category are winter visitors. That is to say they live in this country during the cold months of the northern winter, leaving in the spring to fly north and breed in a cooler climate. Many of them, especially some of the Waders, fly great distances and nest in the subarctic tundra country of Manchuria and Siberia. People who have lived in a temperate climate will be familiar with the opposite state of affairs, in which the migrant birds arrive in the spring to breed and depart again in the autumn.

The spring breeding season of birds in cold climates is determined by the upsurge of insect and other life after the winter, which provides food for the nestlings. In our region there is no season particularly

---

[1] That is the peninsula south of the Isthmus of Kra and the islands close to it, including Singapore.

I

characterized in this way and one might expect the breeding of the resident birds to continue throughout the year, or be related to the not very well defined wetter and drier seasons. Curiously enough neither condition prevails; although nests of some species may be found throughout the year, the main breeding season is in the early months, about January to April in the south of the Malay Peninsula, two or three months later in the north. The correlation is not with the main rainy season, as this is earlier in the north than in the south. Most of our birds follow this breeding rhythm fairly closely, but the Herons, and perhaps some of the other water-birds have their nesting season later in the year, and the larger birds of prey nest rather before the main breeding season.

Both the English and Latin names of the birds in this book are those adopted by B. King and E. C. Dickinson for their forthcoming *Field-Guide to the Birds of Continental South-East Asia* (Collins). The Latin or zoological nomenclature provides all animals with two names, a specific one which identifies it precisely and a generic one which defines its closest relationship with other species. A group of animals included under one generic name is called a genus (plural, genera); the word species is the same in singular and plural. The genus is put first, the species second, just as John Smith is printed Smith, John in a directory.

Thus both the flowerpeckers described in this book belong to the genus *Dicaeum,* one being the species *Dicaeum cruentatum* (the Scarlet-backed Flowerpecker), the other *Dicaeum trigonostigmum* (the Orange-bellied Flowerpecker).

In some bird books, however (including the earlier edition of this one), a third Latin word is added to the end of the Latin name, which thus becomes trinomial. This is because in groups of animals which have been very intensively studied (and none have been more so than birds) it has been found that populations obviously belonging to the same species, but inhabiting different territories (or different environments such as the mountains and lowlands), are distinguishable. These are recognized and named as *subspecies* or *races,* and are designated by a subspecific name which is added to the generic and specific names.

In most cases, subspecific distinctions are subtle differences in colour or in size, and are too fine to be discerned by the observer in the field. Hence all subspecific names have been omitted from this edition, with one exception. This is the Blue-winged Pitta, of which two subspecies occur in the Peninsula: these cannot be distinguished from each other in the field, but occur in different places and at different seasons. The Lesser Blue-winged Pitta, *Pitta moluccensis moluccensis,* is a migrant to the Peninsula, where it stays from October to April, living on the edge of forest and sometimes entering gardens and villages. The Large Blue-winged Pitta, *Pitta moluccensis megarhyncha,* breeds in the Peninsula and is present throughout the year, but is strictly confined to the mangrove belt of the west coast.

In the brief descriptions which head the account given of each species an attempt has been made to indicate size by a figure representing the length. This is arrived at by laying the body of a bird flat on its back and measuring from bill to tail-tip. In cases where the figure is rendered unrealistic by a very long bill or tail, this is mentioned. Examples of normally proportioned birds and their lengths are: Sparrow, 5 inches; Magpie-Robin, 8 inches; Common Myna, 10 inches; Domestic Pigeon, 15 inches.

For those who wish to carry the study of West Malaysian birds further, there are several comprehensive books available in reference libraries, but at the time of writing (January 1968) only one other book is in print. *An Introduction to Malayan Birds* by G. C. Madoc, published by the Malayan Nature Society, though not comprehensive, describes considerably more species than we have space for here and gives a very clear and readable account of their habits.

Our thanks are due to Dr. I.C.T. Nisbet for notes and corrections in this edition, including revision of the nomenclature. There have been considerable changes in English and Latin nomenclature. This may cause some confusion and this is regretted, but it forms part of an effort by ornithologists to establish a stable and world–wide system of names and will be used in all Asian bird books from now on.

# SEA-BIRDS

The flocks of Gulls that crowd round ships in European and temperate Asian seaports are not a feature of the Malaysian coasts, but several species of Terns live and breed with us, mostly on small islands some distance out to sea. Terns are slender, graceful birds with narrow, pointed wings and usually forked tails. They feed on little fish swimming near the surface, diving down on them with a splash and immediately rising again. Our commonest species are mainly white. One of the Gannets or Boobies and one species of Frigate Bird are seen quite frequently from ships in our waters.

LITTLE TERN (*Sterna albifrons*)[1]

**Chamar Kĕchil**[1]

Length 10 inches. Very pale grey above, white below, with some black on the crown, this dainty, graceful little bird appears mainly white in flight. In winter it lives round the coasts but resorts in the summer season to places where there are extensive sandbanks, to breed. These are mainly on the shore and up the larger rivers of the east coast. The eggs are laid in a depression in the sand; they are pale brown spotted with darker brown and lavender.

BLACK-NAPED TERN (*Sterna sumatrana*)                    Fig. 1

**Chamar**

Length 13½ inches. White, very pale grey above with a black band encircling the back and sides of the head and ending on each side in front of the eye. The feet and bill are black. This is the commonest of three species of Terns that nest on rocky uninhabited islets off our coasts. It is found on both sides of the Peninsula and its breeding season is from May to July or August.

The eggs are pale brown or buff blotched with dark brown and lavender. Two are usually laid, either in a depression on a rock ledge or reef, or in a shallow nest of rock fragments.

[1] Throughout the book Latin names are printed in *italics*, Malay names in heavy type.

Fig. 1. Black-naped Tern.

Nesting colonies of the BRIDLED TERN (*Sterna anaethetus*) are known near Tioman Island off the east coast and in the Malacca Strait. It is a little larger than the Black-naped Tern and its upper parts are sooty black.

The ROSEATE TERN (*Sterna dougallii*), **Chamar Jambu**, can be distinguished from the Black-naped Tern by its having a black top to the head, instead of a band encircling it, and by the bright red feet and bill. Both these Terns develop a rosy flush on the breast in the breeding season, but it is more distinct in the Roseate Tern. This bird also frequents small islands and breeds off the east coast.

Sea-voyagers in the Malacca Strait will quite frequently see the BROWN BOOBY (*Sula leucogaster*, Fig. 2), **Angsa Laut.** This is a large, heavily built bird (length 32 inches), sooty brown above and on neck and breast, otherwise white below, a sharp line of demarcation between the brown and white of the underparts; bill sharp and

Fig. 2. Brown Booby.

dagger-like. Like other Boobies and Gannets they fly with steady, fairly rapid wing-beats, gliding at intervals and feed by diving into the sea for fish. They nest in colonies and the Brown Booby breeds in large numbers on Pulau Perak, a small desolate island about seventy miles north-west of Penang.

The LESSER FRIGATEBIRD (*Fregata ariel*, Fig. 3), **Simbang,** has a

Fig. 3. Lesser Frigate bird, female above, male below.

PLATE 1. A. White-breasted Waterhen; B. Slaty-breasted Rail; C. Little Heron; D. Reef Egret.

INCHES

C

D

A

B

*Plate* 1

A

B

C

D

INCHES

*Plate* 2

wing-span of six feet and is the smallest of the Frigatebirds, though none of the others are much larger. It is black, with or without some white on the underparts, the wings long, narrow and sharply curved, the tail deeply forked. These birds can be seen near the Aroa Islands in the Malacca Strait and around Tioman Island in the South China Sea; they may breed at these localities but this is not established. They have wonderful powers of flight and are usually seen soaring at a great height with motionless outstretched wings. This mode of flight and the deeply forked tail distinguish a Frigatebird immediately from a Booby.

# WATERFOWL

The birds referred to under this heading are those which frequent and swim in fresh water, swamps, ponds and rivers. Mud, buffalo-leeches and other hazards deter most people from venturing far into country of this sort, and so most waterfowl are rarely seen. The few that are described here either stray frequently away from their home in the marshes or can be seen on open water.

WHITE-BREASTED WATERHEN (*Amaurornis phoenicurus*)     Plate 1A
**Ruak-ruak**

Length 13 inches. Grey above, white below and chestnut under the tail, this is the commonest of all our waterfowl and the only one frequently seen away from really swampy country. It seldom flies and is usually seen walking on its long legs, with its short tail erect, searching for food by the roadside or even in one's garden, if there is swamp not far away. Its call, '*u-wak u-wak*', which gives it its Malay name, is loud and many times repeated and can often be heard in rice-fields and marshes. It is a bird of the lowlands but, rather surprisingly, has found its way to the inhabited area of Cameron Highlands.

The nest may be among reeds in a swamp, in long grass or in a low bush. Three to five eggs are laid, pale buff, blotched all over with reddish-brown and grey.

PLATE 2.   A. Cattle Egret; B. Cinnamon Bittern ♂, ♀; C. Redshank; D. Red Junglefowl ♂, ♀.

**Sintar**

Length 9 inches. This small Rail is fairly common in low-lying swampy country. It is smaller than the Waterhen, brown barred with white above, the flanks barred black and white and the breast bluish-grey, head and neck chestnut. The nest is made on the ground, well concealed and usually near water; eggs very much like those of the Waterhen but smaller.

The MOORHEN (*Gallinula chloropus*), **Ruak-ruak hitam,** is quite unmistakable, appearing black at a distance (there is a little white in the plumage) with a bright red 'shield' above the bill. It is not very common and is only mentioned here because the mining pools near Kuala Lumpur are one of the places where it can nearly always be seen.

Wild ducks are poorly represented in Malaysia and all but one species are definitely rare. This one, the LESSER WHISTLING DUCK (*Dendrocygna javanica*), **Bělibis,** is a small duck, length 16 inches, sometimes seen in flocks in rice-fields and on open water, most frequently near the east coast. It is brown all over, head, neck and underparts paler, chestnut round the tail. It nests on the ground in or near marshes and lays about eight creamy-white eggs.


# HERONS, EGRETS AND BITTERNS

These are all fairly large birds with very long legs, long neck and a long dagger-like bill. Most of them frequent marshes, rivers or the sea-shore and feed on fish, frogs and other creatures living in the water. Some of the Herons and Egrets nest in colonies, many nests being built close together, usually in trees; the Bitterns nest singly among reeds in marshy country. Egrets can be regarded as white Herons and Bitterns as brown ones.

All these birds have a characteristic appearance in flight. The wings are broad, the head and neck are drawn back between the shoulders, and the long legs stuck out behind.

LITTLE HERON (*Butorides striatus*)                    Plate 1c
**Puchong Bakau, Puchong Kĕladi**

Dark greenish-grey above, light grey below, this is the commonest Heron of the region though it is far less conspicuous than the Reef Egret or other Egrets. It is essentially a bird of mangrove swamps and river banks near the sea, and people who frequent such places will often see these little Herons, walking rather furtively over the mud and among the mangrove roots, or perched on a low branch near the water.

It breeds singly or in small colonies, usually of not more than ten nests, in mangrove or other trees near water. The nests are platforms of twigs and three eggs are laid, pale greenish-blue with a chalky texture. Two distinct breeding seasons have been recorded: January and February and June to August.

REEF EGRET (*Egretta sacra*)                          Plate 1d
**Puchong Batu**

Length 23 inches. A most curious feature of this bird is that it occurs in two distinct colour phases; the plumage may be either dark slaty grey or pure white. The two forms are not related to season, age or sex and both occur together, though in our region the dark phase is by far the more common. Occasionally intermediate 'piebald' birds are seen. This is a bird of the sea-shore, most often seen singly at low tide, hunting for crabs and molluscs, on rocky shores and small islands and on coral reefs, less frequently on sandy shores.

It nests on small islands; the nest is quite substantial and made of sticks and is placed on a ledge of rock or in a low bush. The pale bluish-green eggs number usually three to five.

CATTLE EGRET (*Bubulcus ibis*)                        Plate 2a
**Bangau**

Length 20 inches. During the northern winter this Egret is pure white, and it is seen in Malaysia mainly in this period, about September to April. Occasionally birds stay for the summer and adopt the breeding plumage of orange-coloured feathers on the head and fore-part of the body, but there is only one record of their breeding in this country, in northern Kelantan.

This beautiful bird is the most frequently seen of the Malaysian

9

Herons. Wherever cattle graze, even in quite heavily populated places like Singapore, flocks of them follow the cows or buffaloes, often perching on their backs. It is said that they pick ticks off the animals, but their main reason for seeking their company is to capture grasshoppers and other insects which are disturbed by the trampling of the cattle. So long as it remains still a grasshopper is almost invisible, but when it hops the birds' sharp eyes can mark it down. Unlike most herons this bird feeds almost entirely on insects.

The Cattle Egret could be confused with the Reef Egret in its white phase, but can be identified by its surroundings. A flock of white Herons in rice-fields or pasture will always be Cattle Egrets; a single one on the shore always a Reef Egret.

The GREAT EGRET (*Egretta alba*), **Bangau besar,** is less common but does breed in the Peninsula, in the extensive mangrove swamps of the Perak and Selangor coasts. There is a small colony of nests on Pulau Kětam near Port Swettenham. It is larger than the Cattle Egret (36 inches) and always pure white, even in the breeding season, which is in August or September.

CINNAMON BITTERN (*Ixobrychus cinnamomeus*)         Plate 2B
**Burong Gělam**

Length 15 inches. Chestnut above, chestnut-buff below, throat white with a dark brown median line; the male brighter chestnut than the female. This is the only species of Bittern that is common in the region, and is an inhabitant of rice-fields and freshwater swamp. Like other Bitterns it has the remarkable habit of resting among withered reeds with the body vertical and the head and neck pointed upwards. Its outline and all its streaky brown markings are thus aligned with the vegetation and it becomes almost invisible.

The nest is placed among reeds in wet situations and consists of a platform made of reeds and raised well above the water, a habit which must serve to protect it from sudden floods. The eggs are chalky white and number two or three.


## WADERS

This large order of birds, which includes Plovers, Snipe, Curlews, Sandpipers, etc., is well represented in this country by winter visitors, but very poorly by resident and breeding species. By far the majority of our Waders fly to the north to breed, many of them nesting on the tundra of Siberia and Manchuria. Most of them leave us in April and May and return in August or September. Some, when they are with us, frequent riversides, swamps and pastures, but many are seen only on open sand- and mud-flats, where they are hard to approach and very hard to identify, since there are numerous species of similar appearance. Only a small selection of the visiting Waders can be described here.

COMMON SANDPIPER (*Actitis hypoleucos*)      Plate 3A
**Kĕdidi**

Length 8 inches. A little brownish-grey bird, white below, with a white bar on the wing, conspicuous when it flies. This is the most frequently seen of our Waders, and occurs, singly or in pairs, occasionally in small parties, on beaches, beside open water and especially along the higher courses of rivers and streams. It penetrates far up into the hills and is a familiar bird in the Cameron Highlands. A few individuals remain throughout the year but it is rarely seen between April and August.

The Malay name **Kĕdidi** is applied indiscriminately to all small Waders like Sandpipers, Stints and the smaller Plovers.

REDSHANK (*Tringa totanus*)      Plate 2C
**Burong Kaki Dian**

Length 11¼ inches. This is one of the commonest of the Waders that frequent the mud-flats and mangrove. It has a long straight bill and is grey above, white on the lower back and underparts, with a white bar on the wing; there appears to be a great deal of white in its plumage when it flies. This feature, the long red legs and its clear piping whistle will serve to distinguish it from others of the long-billed Waders. It is seen both singly and in flocks.

PINTAIL SNIPE (*Capella stenura*)      Plate 3B
**Tĕtirok, Burong Bĕrkek**

Length 10¼ inches of which 2½ inches are accounted for by the straight, slender bill. The plumage is mottled and barred with a rich pattern of black, rufous-brown and buff, paler on the underparts. This and two other less common species of Snipe visit the Peninsula in great numbers between September and April, and are to be found in low-lying grasslands, marshes and rice-fields. When disturbed Snipe rise very suddenly and fly low with a zigzag course, uttering a curious '*zzak zzak zzak*'.

The Pintail Snipe is so called because the seven outer tail feathers are stiff and narrow. Two other species, distinguished by not possessing this feature, visit our region in far smaller numbers. They are the COMMON SNIPE (*Capella gallinago*) and SWINHOE'S SNIPE (*Capella megala*). They are not easy to tell apart, and neither can be distinguished from the Pintail in the field.

If you must kill birds for sport, Snipe are by far the best quarry to hunt in our country. Great skill with the gun and a lot of strenuous walking are required to obtain a good bag of them.

LESSER GOLDEN PLOVER (*Pluvialis dominica*)
**Burong Kĕriyut**

Length 10 inches, the bill is short. Black mottled with buff and yellow above and, in winter plumage, white below. Just after arrival in September and just before departure in the spring, some birds show traces of the black breeding-plumage on the underparts. During their stay with us these Plovers live in flocks by the shore and also on open grassy places like race-courses, air-fields and football-fields. The call is a melodious double whistle, '*kuill kuill*'.


# GAME BIRDS

This order of birds includes Pheasants, Partridges, Quail, the Domestic Fowl and its ancestor the Junglefowl. They are less represented in Malaysia than on the Asian mainland, and most of the species which do occur in this country live in the jungle and are rarely seen.

They are birds which spend most of their time on the ground. They nest on the ground and their young are active almost as soon as they are hatched. Baby game birds are always covered with down and are very pretty and attractive.

The Button Quail is included here although it is not a true Quail and belongs to a distinct order. This is apparent if its feet are examined, for it has only three toes; the true game birds have an additional hind toe, making four.

COMMON BUTTON QUAIL (*Turnix suscitator*)       Plate 3c
**Puyoh**

Length 5¼ inches. A small round bird about the size of a sparrow. Both sexes are mottled brown above and buff below spotted and barred with black, and have only three toes. The female is more richly coloured than the male and has a black patch on the throat and breast, and she is also a little larger. It is unusual for a female bird to have brighter plumage than her mate, for normally she incubates the eggs and requires to be inconspicuously coloured for the sake of concealment, especially if the nest is on the ground. Here, however, the usual roles of the sexes are reversed, for the female courts the male, displaying her handsome black shirt-front for his admiration, and fighting other females for possession of him. It is she, of course, who lays the eggs, but her husband has the job of sitting on them until they hatch and then bringing up the family.

Button Quails are common in open grassy country of all kinds, such as golf-courses, market-gardens and recently burnt-off clearings. The nest is made on the ground in a clump of grass, and the long stems surrounding it are pulled together to form a roof over the top. Usually four eggs are laid, pear-shaped, greyish-white thickly speckled with dark brown, most densely around the broader end. Nesting season, January to June.

BLUE-BREASTED QUAIL (*Coturnix chinensis*)       Plate 3D
**Pikau**

Length 5 inches. This bird is similar in size, appearance and habits to the last, but here the male has the underparts brightly coloured, throat black and white, breast and flanks slaty blue, chestnut-brown further back. The female is pale brown below, barred with black, and not very easy to distinguish at sight from the male

13

Button Quail; in the hand the Blue-breasted Quail's four toes identify it immediately.

This bird lives and makes its nest in all kinds of grassland, and its breeding habits are normal, the care of the eggs and young being undertaken by the female. The nest is usually made among tall grass, often lalang, and is just a shallow depression lined with dry grass. Five to seven eggs are laid, pear-shaped, pale olive-brown finely speckled with black. Nesting seas n, January to August.

RED JUNGLEFOWL (*Gallus gallus*)                              Plate 2D
**Ayam Hutan, Ayam Děnak**

Length of male 27 inches, of which nearly half is tail, female 17 inches. The cock is very handsome, black, the tail iridescent, and flame coloured on the back. The hen is mostly brown with the back yellow. This is our commonest game bird, except for Quail, and much sought after by sportsmen. Its natural habitat is the drier parts of the lowland jungle, but it is often seen in clearings, beside rivers and particularly on oil-palm estates. The call of the male is a crow, much like that of a domestic cock, but higher pitched. The bird is polygamous, each cock having a number of wives, and jungle cocks often dispute, successfully, the marital rights of domestic roosters in kampongs adjoining jungle.

The nest is a scrape in the ground made anywhere where there is good cover, such as the cover-crop planted on estates: about six creamy-white eggs are laid. They can easily be hatched under a domestic hen and the birds become quite tame, but are of course liable to wander away when they grow up.

The Red Junglefowl is the evolutionary ancestor of all domestic poultry.

Several kinds of Pheasants occur in the Peninsula, but almost all are birds of the forest and rarely seen. Finest of them is the GREAT ARGUS (*Argusianus argus*), **Kuang**. Its plumage is intricately patterned in shades of brown and on the wings of the male are rows of large eye-like markings, delicately shaded in such a way that they seem to stand out from the feathers. Very few people have seen a wild Great Argus, but it is not really rare in forest, and its loud double call, '*kuang kuang*', can frequently be heard in this sort of country.

PLATE 3.   A. Common Sandpiper; B. Pintail Snipe; C. Common Button Quail ♂, ♀; D. Blue-breasted Quail ♂, ♀.

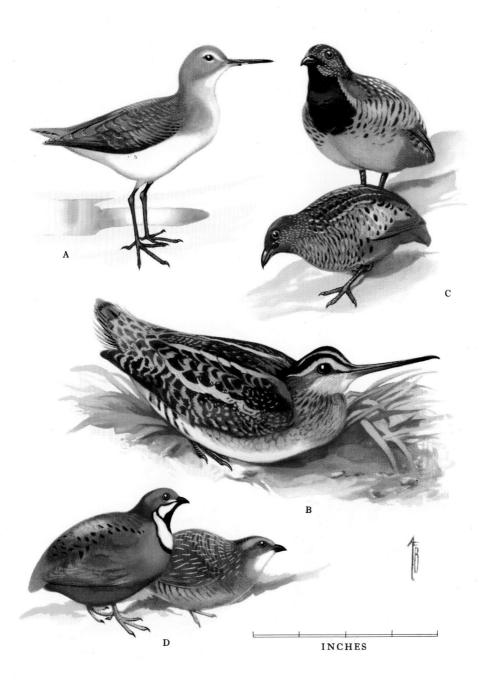

A

C

B

D

INCHES

*Plate* 3

INCHES

A

B

C

D

*Plate* 4

The GREEN PEAFOWL (*Pavo muticus*), **Mĕrak**, is not uncommon in the eastern States. The appearance of a Peacock is too familiar to need description. They are seldom seen in the Peninsula except along the coastal roads of Trengganu and Pahang; there they not infrequently delight and astonish drivers and their companions by flying up or running for cover in front of a car.

## PIGEONS AND DOVES

This family of birds is well represented in our region by nineteen species. They are rather plump birds, some of them much given to posturing and cooing to each other at courtship. They live entirely on vegetable food, fruit or seeds, and the nesting habits are curiously uniform. The nest is almost always a slight platform of twigs in a tree and usually two white eggs are laid, though some species lay only one.

They fall into three groups, the large IMPERIAL PIGEONS, the smaller GREEN PIGEONS, both of which live among trees and often consort in flocks, and thirdly the DOVES. These last are fairly small birds with pointed wings and rather long tails, and they spend much of their time on the ground searching for the seeds on which they feed.

MOUNTAIN IMPERIAL PIGEON (*Ducula badia*)                Plate 4A

**Pĕrgam Bukit**

Length 16½ inches. Head, neck and underparts grey except for the white chin and throat, purplish above, tip of tail grey. Although this is a mountain bird it is probably the most often seen of the Imperial Pigeons. Any visitor to the hill stations who notices birds is likely to see them flying across the valleys, and to hear their deep, resonant call, '*whoo-whoo*'. Nests have been found in the early months of the year and a single white egg is laid.

The GREEN IMPERIAL PIGEON (*Ducula aenea*), **Pĕrgam**, of the lowlands resembles the last in size and general appearance, but is bronzy green on the back. It is a local bird, most often seen in the mangrove of the west coast.

PLATE 4. A. Mountain Imperial Pigeon; B. Pink-necked Pigeon ♂, ♀; C. Spotted-necked Dove; D. Zebra Dove.

PINK-NECKED PIGEON (*Treron vernans*) Plate 4B
**Punai**

Length 10½ inches. This is the commonest of a number of closely allied species, both sexes being distinguished from any of the others by a yellow bar on the wing, and the male by the mauve-pink neck. Apart from this the male has the head grey and an orange patch on the breast, but these features are shared with three of the other Green Pigeons; the female is almost entirely green.

This is a common bird of the lowlands near the coast, where it is much sought after as a sporting bird. Its habit of congregating in large flocks and flying on more or less constant routes between feeding and roosting grounds makes it a particular favourite of the man with a gun, and it is just big enough to be worth cooking. These little Pigeons feed on fruits and berries of all kinds, for which they visit a variety of trees, figs, palms, the Straits Rhododendron and others. The call is a curious bubbling, whistling sound, very different from the 'coo' of most kinds of Pigeons. The nest is a little platform of sticks in a small tree and two white eggs are laid.

The most common of the other Green Pigeons is the slightly smaller THICK-BILLED PIGEON (*Treron curvirostra*), **Punai Daun,** which is found inland and in the foothills of the mountains. The male is maroon above and green below. Both sexes have an area of green skin surrounding the eyes, a feature which distinguishes the bird at once from the Pink-necked Pigeon.

SPOTTED-NECKED DOVE (*Streptopelia chinensis*) Plate 4C
**Tĕkukur**

Length 12 inches. Earthy brown above, paler below, with a patch of rather fine black and white chequer markings on each side and over the back of the neck. This last feature, together with its larger size, distinguishes it from the next species.

This very tame and attractive little Dove is one of our most familiar birds. It seems to be confined to gardens and cultivated areas and is one of the species that has recently spread from the lowlands (its normal habitat) to the hill stations. It is most frequently seen in pairs, occasionally in small flocks. The call is a soft cooing note of three or four syllables. These Doves spend most of their time walking about on the ground searching for the seeds on which they feed, and usually fly only a little way and alight in a tree when approached.

The nest is of the usual pigeon and dove type, a little platform of sticks in a bush or low tree, and two white eggs are laid.

ZEBRA DOVE (*Geopelia striata*)                                    Plate 4D

**Balam, Měrbok**

Length 9 inches. This species is coloured much like the last, but is faintly barred all over with black and lacks the chequered patch on the neck; it is also smaller. It is not quite so generally distributed as the Spotted-necked Dove, but is fairly common, frequents similar situations and is perhaps even more tame. It does not coo like other Doves, but calls with a sort of melodious chuckling note.

Both these little Doves are considered lucky by the country people, who never shoot or molest them; probably this is why they are so tame. Unfortunately they pay for this privilege by being very often kept in little cages, much too small and cramped for them to be comfortable and happy. Their tameness and ability to subsist on a diet of seeds makes them easy to keep in captivity, and even when so imprisoned they call softly and frequently.


# BIRDS OF PREY

This order of birds, which includes Eagles, Hawks, Kites, Vultures, etc., is well represented, and some of our largest and finest birds belong to it. Most of these birds are predatory, the larger ones feeding on mammals, other birds, reptiles or, in some cases, mainly on fish; some of the smaller species include insects in their diet. The Kites live mainly, the Vultures entirely, by scavenging. The descriptions given here refer to adult birds; when immature most of the larger birds of prey are brown, variously mottled and barred or streaked, but lacking distinctive markings.

The breeding season of our large birds of prey is earlier than that of most of the smaller birds, extending from December to February or March.

WHITE-BELLIED SEA EAGLE (*Haliaeetus leucogaster*)    Plate 5A
**Lang Laut, Lang Siput**

Length 28 inches. The head, neck and underparts are white, the upper parts grey and the tail black at the base, white towards the tip. This very fine Eagle is a common bird all round our coasts and on the off-shore islands, and is most often seen soaring in circles at a great height. Its food consists of fish, crabs and sea-snakes—as they swim on the surface these reptiles form an easy prey and the Eagles undoubtedly destroy large numbers of them. Crabs are dropped from a height on to rocks in order to break the shell. Since they take all their food from the sea these Eagles are completely harmless and should never be shot or molested.

The nest is built in the top of a high tree. It is used year after year and constantly added to, so that one that has been long in use may consist of a small cartload of dead sticks. There are always several nests existing on Singapore and Penang Islands, as well as at numerous other coastal localities. Two eggs are laid, chalky white without markings.

BRAHMINY KITE (*Haliastur indus*)    Plate 5B
**Lang Merah**

Length 19 to 20 inches. Head, throat and breast white, elsewhere bright chestnut. In the white of the underparts the shafts of the feathers are dark and an effect of fine black streaks is produced. The habits of this bird are at variance with its handsome appearance, for it lives entirely as a scavenger. Although occasionally seen inland it is mainly a coastal bird and frequents harbours and fishing villages, picking up offal and any floating rubbish around ships. Its cry is a high-pitched '*miaow*', rather like a cat.

It nests usually in mangrove forest in fairly tall trees; the nest is built of sticks and lined with dry mud. Two eggs are laid, chalky white with faint brown markings. Breeding season December to February and sometimes later.

CHANGEABLE HAWK-EAGLE (*Spizaetus cirrhatus*)    Plate 5C
**Lang Hindek**

Length 26 inches. This large Eagle exists in two distinct colour phases. In the dark one the whole plumage is dark sooty brown; in the lighter phase (which is illustrated on Plate 5) it is lighter brown above, the underparts buff or almost white with conspicuous dark streaks. The case is similar to that described for the Reef Egret (p. 9) and in both the variation is quite independent of age, sex or season of the year. The case of the Eagle is less simple as the light phase is variable and intermediate specimens not uncommon.

This is one of the most often seen of our large inland birds of prey. It spends much of its time soaring at a great height so that it appears as a black silhouette, and it is impossible to make out the colour. It feeds on any animals and birds it can catch, and cannot be said to be harmless as it frequently takes chickens.

The nest is a large structure made of sticks, built in the top of a tall tree. Only one egg is laid, chalky white, sometimes with faint brown markings.

CRESTED SERPENT EAGLE (*Spilornis cheela*)         Plate 5D
**Lang Kuik**

Length 21 inches. Dark brown above, reddish-brown below marked with white spots on the belly. There is a broad white band across the underside of the tail and a narrower one along the hinder margins of the wings; these are the best means of distinguishing the bird in flight, if it is low enough for any colours to be seen. It has a prominent crest of black and white feathers on the head which may be conspicuous when the bird is at rest, but is often laid flat so that it is invisible. This eagle has a wild and far-carrying whistling call, 'Kweee-Kwee' which it utters while flying high in the air.

The Serpent Eagle is so called because it is supposed to feed on snakes. These reptiles may form part of its diet, but certainly do not comprise the whole of it; like the last species this Eagle is a bad chicken thief. The nest and eggs are smaller than those of the Hawk Eagle but otherwise similar.

BLACK-THIGHED FALCONET (*Microhierax fringillarius*)
**Rajawali, Lang Bĕlalang**

Length 6½ inches. With this species we pass abruptly from Eagles to one of the smallest birds of prey in the world, for it is hardly larger than a sparrow. It is black above, marked with white on the head, the throat white and the rest of the underparts chestnut. It is most often seen in open country with scattered trees, such as jungle clearings and the more park-like and spacious kind of gardens. It feeds mainly on large insects (**Lang Bĕlalang** means Grasshopper Hawk'), but will kill birds almost as big as itself. In defence of its nest it will fiercely attack anything or anybody.

The usual site of the nest is in a hole in a tree. Like those of almost all birds with this habit of nesting the eggs are white and unmarked; four or five eggs are laid.

A bird of prey often seen flying over rice-fields is the BLACK-WINGED KITE (*Elanus caeruleus*), **Lang Tikus**. Length      inches. It is a handsome bird, pale grey above with a black patch on each wing, head and underparts white, so that it looks largely white from below. It feeds on rats, as implied by its Malay name, and is a useful as well as a beautiful bird.

The JAPANESE SPARROWHAWK (*Accipiter gularis*), **Lang Sewah,** is a winter visitor to our region and quite common, especially near the coast. It is grey (male) or brown (female) above and barred pinkish-brown and white below, the tail long and the wings rather short and rounded; length 11 inches. It preys on small birds.

## OWLS

Although Owls are 'birds of prey' in their habits, they are very distinct from the Eagles, Kites and Hawks of the last chapter. Almost all Owls are nocturnal and have very large eyes, forwardly directed and set in a round, flat face. Their plumage is soft and downy, making their flight entirely silent, and is usually brown, intricately marked with darker and lighter shades; some have the underparts white. They sleep in dark or dimly lighted places in the day, and their sombre brown colours serve to keep them hidden. An Owl discovered and disturbed in the day has an unhappy time; it is dazzled by the bright light, and small birds, taking advantage of its helplessness, mob it mercilessly. The eggs of all Owls are round and glossy white.

MALAY FISH OWL (*Ketupa ketupu*)                    Plate 6A
**Burong Hantu, Tumbok Kĕtampi**

Length 18 inches. A large Owl, brown marked with buff above, buff below streaked with black. It is common near the coast and is most often seen flying at dusk over open country. The eggs are laid, without any attempt at nest-building, in a hollow tree, or sometimes in the abandoned nest of some other large bird.

COLLARED SCOPS OWL (*Otus bakkamoena*)              Plate 6B
**Burong Jampok**

Length 9 inches. This is the smallest of our common Owls and has the usual streaked brown plumage, dark above, buff below, and a pale buff ring or collar on the neck. There is a pair of conspicuous feather tufts on the head having the appearance of ears. This little owl frequently visits gardens in the lowlands, even in towns, and sometimes enters houses at night, when it is rendered confused and helpless by the bright lights. Its call is a hollow, mournful note, 'whoop' which descends in pitch and sounds disyllabic to some ears. The nest is usually made in a hollow tree or stump and two eggs are laid. Breeding season, February to April.

The BROWN HAWK OWL (*Ninox scutulata*), **Punggok,** is intermediate in size between the two species already described, length about 11 inches, and is uniform dark brown above and streaked with reddish-brown, buff and white below, the wings long and pointed. This is a common bird but far more often heard than seen. Its call is a musical double hoot 'whoo-oop' which rises in pitch. It is said to feed mostly on insects.

## PARROTS

Parrots are not conspicuous among Malaysian birds, either in number of species or individuals. They are confined to the lowlands and are most often seen in small flocks in the vicinity of jungle.

LONG-TAILED PARAKEET (*Psittacula longicauda*)
**Bayan**

Length of male 16 inches, including 10 inches of tail. Green, yellowish below, some blue above, head green on top, elsewhere rose-pink, with a black streak behind the bill. The central tail feathers much elongated in the male, less so in the female, whose plumage is more purely green on the body and has less pink on the head.

These birds may be seen occasionally flying swiftly in small flocks over jungle clearings. It is becoming a serious pest on oil palm estates in Johore, and will probably increase and spread to other parts of the country. It is possible to confuse them with Green Pigeons, but the long tail and the habit of screaming harshly in flight are distinctive. The nest is made in a hole high up in a tree and two glossy white eggs are laid. Breeding season, about January and February.

The MALAYAN HANGING LORIKEET (*Loriculus galgulus*), Sĕrindit, is a Parrot the size of a Sparrow, bright green, the back yellow and red, a patch of red on the throat and a blue spot on the crown. This coloration is vivid in the male, less so in the female, which lacks the red throat. Lorikeets are not abundant but are fairly frequently seen in small parties in cultivated country where jungle is not far away. They are great favourites as cage-birds. The nest, like that of nearly all Parrots, is made in a hole in a tree and the eggs are white.

## CUCKOOS

The English name of this group of birds is derived from the call of the one species which occurs, as a summer visitor, in Britain. The Cuckoos are much better represented in the Peninsula, twenty-five species having been recorded. Some of them, including the European bird, have the remarkable habit of placing their eggs in other birds' nests, where they are brooded by the foster-mother. When the young Cuckoo hatches it throws out the eggs (or young if they have also hatched) for whose accommodation the nest was built, and the parental instinct of its owners is diverted entirely to the changeling. Cuckoos usually choose the nests of birds much smaller than themselves (and lay very small eggs for their size), and so one sometimes sees the curious spectacle of a nearly fledged Cuckoo being fed by birds so small that they must stand on its back to place their

PLATE 5. A. White-bellied Sea Eagle; B. Brahminy Kite; C. Changeable Hawk-Eagle; D. Crested Serpent Eagle.

INCHES

A

D

C

B

*Plate* 5

B

A

C

D

INCHES

*Plate 6*

offering in its bill. As I have said, not all Cuckoos have this rather disreputable method of breeding.

None of our common species say '*cuckoo*', but most of them have a distinctive and monotonous call, by which they can often be recognized more easily than by their appearance.

PLAINTIVE CUCKOO (*Cacomantis merulinus*)                     Plate 7A
**Burong Mati Anak**

Length 8 inches. Head, neck and upper breast grey, upper parts brown, underparts rufous-buff; the inside of the bill bright red. This small Cuckoo is often heard but very seldom seen. It has the habit of sitting concealed in the top of a leafy tree and uttering its two very distinct calls. One of these consists of a dismal, tuneless series of seven or more notes in a descending scale, the first ones the longest. The other is a repeated phrase sounding rather like '*keep the sweet, keep the sweet*' in an ascending scale. Both calls are plaintive in quality, and the Malay name 'Dead Child Bird' is an apt, if rather macabre, comment on them. On the other hand the popular name 'Brainfever Bird' rather overstates the case.

This is one of the parasitic Cuckoos and lays its eggs in the nests of small birds such as Tailorbirds.

The BANDED BAY CUCKOO (*Cacomantis sonneratii*) is of approximately the same size as the last and has similar habits, but its appearance is very distinct; it is brown above, white below, barred both above and below with black. It has a monotonous call with a rising scale, but difficult to describe in words, and is also a parasitic species.

GREATER COUCAL (*Centropus sinensis*)                          Plate 6C
**Bubut, But-but**

Length 21 inches of which about half is tail. The head, neck, underparts and tail are black, the back and wings bright chestnut. This large, clumsy-looking bird is very common in open scrub country with plenty of bushes and undergrowth, especially near rivers. It is frequently seen from the train and when driving along the main roads. It flies low and rather slowly and never very far at a time. The call is a deep, loud '*boot-boot-boot-boot*'. The Coucal builds its own nest, a globular structure of grass with a large entrance

PLATE 6. A. Malay Fish Owl; B. Collared Scops Owl; C. Greater Coucal; D. Chestnut-breasted Malkoha.

hole on one side, in undergrowth or bushes. Usually two eggs are laid, pure white.

The LESSER COUCAL (*Centropus toulou*) is very similar in appearance but a good deal smaller, length 15 inches. The body and wings are coloured much as in the Greater Coucal but the back is duller brown. This bird is at least as common as the larger species, perhaps more so, and has similar habits but occurs in more open country. The nest is usually built close to the ground in thick grass. Breeding season, March to May.

CHESTNUT-BREASTED MALKOHA (*Phaenicophaeus curvirostris*) Plate 6D

Length 18 inches. Dark shining green above, chestnut below, the head dark grey with the skin round the eye red and the bill pale green; tail dark green tipped with chestnut. A fairly common bird in secondary forest in the lowlands.

Equally common in similar country is the smaller RAFFLES' MALKOHA (*Phaenicophaeus chlorophaeus*), length 13 inches. Here the sexes differ: male chestnut above and on the head, paler below; female dark chestnut above with the head, neck and underparts pale grey. Both sexes have the tail long, black tipped with white, and both the bill and the skin round the eye bluish-green.

These two species are chosen to represent the Malkohas, of which half a dozen are found in our region and several are quite common. All but one, which is rather rare, have the bill green and all have a long tail and the habit of climbing and scrambling about among the branches of trees. The call is of two kinds, a discordant squawk and a mewing sound, like a cat. They build their own nests, platforms of sticks placed in a fork of a tree, and lay two white eggs. They are variously named in Malay: **Burong Chĕnok, Burong Sanok, Burong Krak** and **Burong Sĕlayak**, but the names do not refer to particular species.

## NIGHTJARS

This is a group of nocturnal birds whose plumage is intricately mottled in shades of brown, rather like that of the Owls, and probably for the same reason, to provide concealment while they sleep during the day. They have long, narrow wings and a widely gaping bill and live by catching flying insects, just as Swifts and Swallows do in the daytime.

Nightjars both sleep and make their nests on the ground and the eggs are protectively coloured, just as the birds are.

LONG-TAILED NIGHTJAR (*Caprimulgus macrurus*)         Plate 7B
**Burong Sĕgan, Burong Malas, Burong Tukang, Burong Kubor**

Length 11½ inches. Greyish-brown mottled with dark brown above and finely barred with black and brown below; there is a patch near the end of each wing and on each side of the tail which is white in the male and buff in the female.

This is the creature commonly known as the 'Tock-tock Bird' from its habit of sitting at night on a post or branch, often in one's garden, and calling loudly and monotonously '*chonk, chonk, chonk*'. The '*chonks*' are frequently in groups of three to five, with a pause between each group, or may be in series of a hundred or more. Some people find the noise very irritating when they are trying to go to sleep.

Although one seldom gets a good look at a Nightjar they can often be seen momentarily when they fly up off the road in front of a car, and the eye glows red in the light of the headlamps just before the bird rises. The eggs are laid on the ground, usually in the open under trees; gardens and rubber estates are favourite situations. The two eggs are pinkish, thickly blotched with lavender and pale reddish-brown. Both they and the plumage of the brooding bird blend remarkably with the background of dead leaves. Breeding season, January to April.

The GREAT EARED NIGHTJAR (*Eurostopodus temminckii*), **Taptibau**, is similar to the last but darker and without the pale patches on wings and tail; there is a pair of feather-tufts on the head which look like ears. It is a jungle bird, common in the lowlands and hill-passes, and can always be seen and heard in the evening at The Gap on the way to Fraser's Hill. It flies rather high and at sunset utters a loud melodious call, 'TAP-*ti-bau*, TAP-*ti-bau*'.

25

# SWIFTS

These are birds which spend a great part of their time on the wing, hawking the flying insects on which they feed. Their wings are narrow and curved and their bodies bullet-like, both adaptations for rapid and effortless flight. They never voluntarily settle on the ground, and drink by skimming over the surface of open water. Swifts are often confused with Swallows, but their anatomy shows them to be really very distinct. Most of them have the curious habit of gluing the materials of the nest together with their saliva. In some of the Swiftlets (*Collocalia*) the nest is made largely or entirely of dried and hardened saliva, and these are the edible birds' nests relished by Chinese gourmets.

Both Swifts and Swallows are collectively known as **Layang-layang** in Malay.

HOUSE SWIFT (*Apus affinis*)          Plate 7c

Length 6 inches. Black with the chin and throat white and a conspicuous white patch on the hinder part of the back. This is by far the commonest of our Swifts and is specially abundant in towns, probably because these afford plenty of suitable nesting-sites. It is most active in the evening, when its shrill chattering cry can be constantly heard from the windows of hotels and upper storey flats.

The nest is made of feathers and grass glued together with saliva, and they are built in clusters, usually on large buildings or under arches. In natural conditions these birds nest on cliffs, and can be found breeding on the steep limestone hills of the centre and north of the country. The provision of artificial cliffs (which is how the Swifts must regard large buildings) must have been of great benefit to this species; it is probably much more numerous now than it was a hundred years ago. Two or three white eggs are laid and the breeding season extends from April to June.

Largest of our Swifts is the GIANT SPINETAIL SWIFT (*Chaetura gigantea*), length 9½ inches. It is black and dark brown with a white patch under the tail, and the tips of the tail feathers are naked, the shafts forming spines over half an inch long. This may be associated with the intense turbulence just behind the bird as it hurtles through

PLATE 7. A. Plaintive Cuckoo; B. Long-tailed Nightjar; C. House Swift; D. Crested Tree-Swift.

INCHES

*Plate* 7

B

D

INCHES

A

C

*Plate* 8

the air, for this large Swift and its close allies are probably the fastest of all animals; the speed of their flight has been estimated at 200 miles an hour. The Spinetail is not uncommon, especially in the mountains, and can be recognized by its large size.

CRESTED TREE-SWIFT (*Hemiprocne longipennis*)                    Plate 7D

Length 8 inches. Iridescent blue-black above, grey, fading to white on the belly, below. A patch just behind the eye is chestnut in the male, green in the female, and both sexes have a crest of feathers on the head which is conspicuous when erected. This is a bird of wooded areas and is most often seen in jungle clearings and rubber estates.

The nest is most extraordinary. It is a tiny half-saucer-shaped structure, made entirely of the bird's saliva, and cemented to the side of a small branch, from which it projects less than an inch. A single white egg is laid, rather large for the size of the bird, so that it is contained in the nest with very little space to spare. When brooding the bird cannot, of course, sit on the nest, it perches on the branch and covers the egg or nestling with its breast feathers. Breeding season, February to July.

WHITE-BELLIED SWIFTLET (*Collocalia esculenta*)

Length 5 inches. Glossy blue-black above, pale grey beneath; much smaller than the House- and Tree-Swifts, the tail less deeply forked. This little Swift is rather local but equally common in the mountains and the lowlands. It is often seen flying in company with other Swifts, and is then easily recognizable by its small size.

It nests in caves, under arches and culverts and often in disused buildings. The nest is a cup-shaped structure, stuck to a vertical or overhanging surface, and made of moss and vegetable fibre cemented with saliva. The edible birds' nests are made by several other species of this genus, which nest in large colonies, usually in caves. The nests are little cups, two inches across, and the most valuable are whitish in colour and composed entirely of matted strings or threads of coagulated saliva. Nests containing feathers or other impurities are less highly priced. The only nesting-place of any importance in West Malaysia is on Tioman Island in the South China Sea.

PLATE 8.    A. White-breasted Kingfisher; B. White-collared Kingfisher; C. Blue-throated Bee-Eater; D. Blue-tailed Bee-Eater.

# KINGFISHERS

Thirteen species of Kingfisher are found in the Peninsula, all brightly coloured and recognizable collectively by the very long and powerful bill, which is coloured black or red, short tail and small legs and feet. Most of them live near water and catch fish by diving in from an overhanging branch, but the two commonest species take much of their food on land, grasshoppers, lizards, snakes or anything else they can catch and overpower. They have raucous voices, often resembling a loud, harsh laugh, and make their nests in burrows, sometimes in banks, sometimes in holes in trees or in termites' nests. The eggs are round and glossy white.

WHITE-BREASTED KINGFISHER (*Halcyon smyrnensis*)     Plate 8A
**Pĕkaka**

Length 10 inches. Back and wings bright blue, throat and breast white, head and belly chocolate, legs and bill red. This is our commonest Kingfisher and a familiar garden bird. It is not particularly attached to the vicinity of water, and feeds on large insects, such as grasshoppers, lizards, frogs, nestling birds, in fact any living creature it can catch and kill. Its usual call is an unmelodious laughing screech. It nests at the end of a tunnel, two to three feet long, which it excavates in the bank of a road or stream. Breeding season, December to May.

WHITE-COLLARED KINGFISHER (*Halcyon chloris*)     Plate 8B
**Pĕkaka**

Length 9½ inches. Blue with white underparts and a white collar round the neck, bill and feet black. This is a coastal bird, most often seen on the shore or among mangrove, but it comes into gardens that are not far from the sea. It probably feeds mainly on small crabs and other crustaceans, but will hunt insects when it strays inland. It has a very loud, harsh cry, '*kree-chah, kree-chah*'. The nest is usually in a burrow excavated among the roots of a fern growing in a tree or in a termites' nest similarly situated.

The COMMON KINGFISHER (*Alcedo atthis*), **Raja Udang**, is a much smaller and more unobtrusive bird (length 6½ inches) and is greenish-blue above, white on the throat, the rest of the underparts chestnut-orange. The bill is black and the feet red. It is rarely seen away from water, both coastal and inland fresh waters, and feeds mainly on little fish, although its Malay name means 'King of the Prawns'.

Not very common, but most striking and conspicuous, is our largest species: the STORK-BILLED KINGFISHER (*Pelargopsis capensis*), **Pĕkaka Mas**. Length 15 inches. It is entirely blue above with the head greyish-brown and the underparts, and a collar round the neck, orange-yellow. The feet and the truly enormous bill are red. It occurs near water in the lowlands, both near the coast and inland.


# BEE-EATERS

These are slender, elegant birds with predominantly blue and green plumage and a long, down-curved bill. In our two common species the centre feathers of the tail are elongated and project beyond the others. They feed by catching insects on the wing, and will eat bees, wasps and other kinds of insects that are avoided by most insecti-vorous birds. They nest in burrows which they excavate in sandy banks or open grassy areas, and some species breed in colonies.

BLUE-THROATED BEE-EATER (*Merops viridis*)                Plate 8c
**Bĕrek-bĕrek**

Length 11 inches, including the elongated tail feathers. Head and forepart of the back chocolate-brown, throat blue, the rest of the plumage blue and green. This beautiful bird is very common in the lowlands and can often be seen in large numbers in the evening, hawking insects over rivers and grasslands; they are often very active just before a rain-storm. When resting they perch on high dead branches of trees and sometimes on telegraph wires.

During the period between October and April this Bee-Eater leaves the lowlands and is seen in the hill stations; possibly a migra-tion to the mountains takes place. Nesting colonies can be found anywhere in open spaces with soft sandy soil, sometimes almost on the sea-shore. The eggs are round, white and glossy and the breeding season April to July.

## BLUE-TAILED BEE-EATER (*Merops philippinus*)      Plate 8D
**Běrek-běrek**

Length 12 inches. All the upper parts, including the head, are blue and green and the underparts green except for the yellow chin and chestnut band on the throat. This Bee-Eater is a winter visitor to most of the Peninsula and replaces the blue-throated species in the lowlands from October to April. Both birds have almost exactly the same habits.

It breeds in Thailand and elsewhere on the continent of Asia, and there are breeding colonies in our most northern states.


## HORNBILLS

These are among the most extraordinary looking birds in the world. They are all large, the bigger ones the size of a domestic turkey, their plumage is black and white and their bills enormous and surmounted by a projection, of the same substance as the bill itself, called the 'casque'. The flight is rather laboured and in some species the noise of the wing-beats is very clearly audible, and often serves to direct attention to the presence of the birds flying overhead. The food consists mainly of fruits and berries.

The Hornbills' breeding habits are as queer as their appearance. The female enters a hole in a tree, which is then plastered up with a kind of cement made of clay, vegetable debris and the bird's droppings, until only a narrow oval slit remains. The hen bird is thus secured against invasion by predatory animals, but is herself a prisoner in the nest during the whole period of egg-laying, incubation and for some time after the eggs have hatched. During this period, which may be as much as three months, the male feeds her with fruit through the narrow door of the nest. When the young birds are ready to leave, the hen breaks down the cement barrier and comes out; presumably she could do this at any time to save herself from starvation if her mate met with an accident.

None of the Hornbills are really common birds, but are so conspicuous that most people living in the country see them from time to time.

PLATE 9. A. Rhinoceros Hornbill; B. Coppersmith Barbet; C. Fire-tufted Barbet.

INCHES

A

INCHES

B

C

*Plate* 9

A

B

C

D

INCHES

*Plate* 10

## SOUTHERN PIED HORNBILL (*Anthracoceros convexus*) Fig. 4
**Burong Kĕlingking, Burong Lilin**

Length 30 inches. Black above, the wings edged with white and white outer tail feathers, neck and breast black, remaining underparts

white. Bill and casque ivory-white, some black on the forepart of the casque. This is our commonest species of Hornbill and is not infrequently seen in flocks along the banks of large rivers; it is the only species which often ventures away from dense jungle. It eats fruit like other Hornbills, but is to some extent predatory as well. The call is a high-pitched, harsh cackle.

It has the normal Hornbill breeding habits, and there is a record of a female being 'imprisoned' in a nesting-hole for eighty-seven days. Two eggs are laid, white when fresh, but conditions in the nesting-hole soon lead to their becoming stained with brown.

Fig. 4. Southern Pied Hornbill.

In the northern States, to about the latitude of Upper Perak, this species is replaced by the NORTHERN PIED HORNBILL (*Anthracoceros albirostris*), which differs in that the outer tail feathers are black, tipped with white, instead of being wholly white. Otherwise the two species are similar in size, appearance and habits.

## RHINOCEROS HORNBILL (*Buceros rhinoceros*) Plate 9A
**Enggang**

Length 48 inches. Black above and on the head and chest, belly and tail white, the latter with a broad black band near the tip: bill ivory-white, casque tinged with orange and red. This is the least rare of the large Hornbills and, although a jungle bird, is not infrequently

PLATE 10. A. Common Golden-backed Woodpecker; B. Malaysian Pygmy Woodpecker; C. Black-and-red Broadbill; D. Blue-winged Pitta.

seen at the edge of clearings and flying over open country, especially in the foothills. The noise of the wings in flight is very loud and has been compared to the strenuous 'chuffing' of a locomotive labouring up a hill. The call is a loud, harsh honk. A nest containing young has been recorded from Pahang in February.

# BARBETS

This is a group of birds allied to the more familiar Woodpeckers. Most of them are small with the plumage predominantly green and patches of bright colour on the head. The bill is very stout and strong. Like Woodpeckers they excavate holes in trees to nest in, but unlike that group they feed on fruit. Barbets are more often heard than seen as most species have a loud and easily recognizable call consisting of one or more syllables monotonously repeated.

COPPERSMITH BARBET (*Megalaima haemacephala*)      Plate 9B
**Burong Tukang, Burong Takau**

Length 6½ inches. Green above, white streaked with dull green below, the head, throat and breast marked with red and yellow. This is the only Barbet that is common in open lowland country through-out most of the region, having spread down from the north during the last 30 years or so. As it is very noisy and frequents gardens and orchards, it is likely to make its presence known as soon as it arrives anywhere. The call is a monotonous *'toonk, toonk, toonk'*, like a hammer beating on metal, and has given the bird its name.

It digs a hole for its nest in the dead branch of a tree and breeds early in the year. The eggs are white.

FIRE-TUFTED BARBET (*Psilopogon pyrolophus*)      Plate 9C

Length 11 inches. Upper parts bright green, underparts lighter green, head and throat marked with dark maroon-brown, lavender, yellow and black; a conspicuous tuft of red bristles at the base of the bill, which is greenish-white, rather large and has a black band half way along it. This is a mountain bird and commonly seen at the hill stations, usually in small parties, scrambling among the twigs and foliage of trees. Its call is most peculiar; it begins with a '*tik, tik, tik*' which becomes more and more rapid until it turns into a buzz, the whole performance being much more like that of a large cicada than of a bird. Nests have been found in the hill stations in February.


# WOODPECKERS

This group is well represented in the region by twenty-five species, many of them brightly and beautifully coloured. They are usually seen clinging erect to the trunk or branch of a tree, sitting back on the stiff feathers of the tail, which are braced against the trunk, and hammering or probing the wood with the powerful, dagger-like bill. Most of them have a loud screaming or laughing cry, and also betray their presence by the rapid tapping of the bill as the bird chisels away the wood, either in search of insects or in the construction of its nesting-tunnel. They have a characteristic dipping or undulating flight.

COMMON GOLDEN-BACKED WOODPECKER (*Dinopium javanense*)

**Bělatok Mas**                                                        Plate 10A

Length 11 inches. Golden-yellow above with the hinder part of the back bright red, tail and the edges of the wings black; underparts white with the feathers black edged, giving a scaly effect. The top of the head is crimson in the male, black and white in the female. This beautiful Woodpecker is common in the lowlands and seems especially attached to coconut palms. Its call is a harsh scream, usually uttered as it flies between one tree and the next.

Nesting-holes are excavated in dead trees, most frequently coconut palms, and three white eggs are laid on a bed of wood chips about ten inches below the entrance hole. Breeding season, February to July.


BAMBOO GREEN WOODPECKER (*Picus vittatus*)

**Bělatok Hijau**

Length 10½ inches. Much less brightly coloured than the last species, dark green above, yellowish-green streaked with black below, a black stripe on each cheek running back to the neck. There is a touch of bright colour in the male, the red top of the head, but it is black in the female. This is a coastal species, especially common on the west coast in open country to the landward side of mangrove swamp. The breeding habits are much the same as in the last species, but there is no particular preference for coconut palms.

MALAYSIAN PYGMY WOODPECKER (*Dendrocopos moluccensis*) Plate 10B
**Bělatok Kěchil**

Length 5½ inches. Black barred with white above, top of head brown; white streaked with black below. There is a red stripe over the eye in the male. This little Woodpecker is common near the coast in places where estates and gardens border on secondary jungle. It has a high-pitched, repeated call, but more often betrays its presence by rapid hammering on a branch. It excavates its nesting-tunnel in small decaying trees or in rotten branches, often tunnelling in at the broken end of a branch. Breeding season, March to July.

Largest of all our Woodpeckers, and not uncommon in lowland jungle, is the GREAT SLATY WOODPECKER (*Mulleripicus pulverulentus*), length 20 inches. This is a bird the size of a crow, grey all over except for the yellow throat. Outside the breeding season these birds congregate in flocks of a dozen or so, a most unusual habit for a Woodpecker.

Closely allied to the Woodpeckers are the Piculets, tiny birds, smaller than a Sparrow. The tail and bill are short, and only their habit of drumming rapidly on bamboo stems reveals their true affinity. The RUFOUS PICULET (*Sasia abnormis*), length 3½ inches, is olive-green above, rufous below and on the back over the tail, which is black; forehead yellow in the male, rufous in the female. It is not uncommon and has a preference for the sort of dry jungle in which bamboo is the dominant plant. To make its nest the bird drills a hole in a living bamboo.


# BROADBILLS

These are small to medium-sized birds with brightly coloured plumage and a broad, flat bill, and are found mainly near water. We have seven species but only one is common.

BLACK-AND-RED BROADBILL (*Cymbirhynchus macrorhynchos*) Plate 10c

**Burong Hujan, Burong Rakit, Burong Ja'jang**

Length 8½ inches. Black above with a white bar on the wing and a crimson patch on the lower back, deep crimson below except for a black band on the breast; bill blue and yellow. This is our only common Broadbill, and is found mainly along river banks, particularly in foothill country, where the rivers flow through jungle.

The bird itself is rather shy and secretive, but its nest is most conspicuous. It is nearly always built over water, hanging from a branch or a bamboo, and consists of an untidy mass of dead leaves, fibre, etc., with a hole in the side giving access to a small chamber in the middle, in which the eggs are laid. It is not always easy to distinguish these nests from the masses of vegetation that are left by falling waters after a flood. Occasionally nests are built overhanging roads. The eggs are white with brown blotches and spots. Breeding season, February to August.

# PITTAS

The Pittas are curious birds whose appearance seems out of harmony with their habits. Nearly all of them are diversely and brilliantly coloured, and yet they are very shy and secretive, living on the ground in thick undergrowth, and for this reason they are seldom seen. All of them have a rather rounded body, short tail and long legs. The nests of those species whose breeding habits are known are domed and built on the ground.

BLUE-WINGED PITTA (*Pitta moluccensis*)                    Plate 10D

**Burong Pachat**

Length 8 inches. Green and bright shining blue above and on the tail, buff below, a patch of bright red under the tail; head brown with a black streak on top and another encircling the crown at the level of the eyes; throat white. This Pitta is a winter visitor to Malaysia and flocks of them arrive in the autumn. They migrate along the coasts and are most often seen on coastal islands and in the mangrove. Migrating birds often fly against the glass of lighthouses and kill themselves, and the Blue-winged Pitta rather frequently falls a victim to this accident.

Although a distinct subspecies the LARGER BLUE-WINGED PITTA (*Pitta moluccensis megarhyncha*) cannot be distinguished in the field from the one just described. The difference in size is hardly perceptible but, if they are placed side by side, the present subspecies can be seen to have a slightly more massive bill and less distinct black streak on the crown. This is a resident bird and is found in mangrove on the west coast and on Singapore Island. The nest is domed and is built on the ground, usually in the drier, landward part of the mangrove swamp or in scrub country adjacent to it. The eggs are white with brown spots; breeding season, April to June.

The HOODED PITTA (*Pitta sordida*) is rather smaller, green above with blue patches on the wings and tail, greenish-blue below with a crimson patch under the tail; head and neck black, a brown patch on the crown. This bird is not uncommon in inland jungle. It is resident, but in winter its numbers are augmented by birds migrating from the north.


## SWALLOWS

The similarity between Swifts and Swallows has already been referred to. In general Swallows have the wings less narrow and sickle-shaped, and more triangular than the Swifts, and it also happens that all our common Swallows have some chestnut-brown on the underparts, and none of the Swifts are so coloured.

They spend much of their time, just as the Swifts do, hawking insects on the wing. They do not breed in colonies, but often flock together outside the breeding season. Like some of the Swifts they are birds which, under natural conditions, nest on cliffs, but will readily use buildings and bridges for the purpose. The nests are made of mud which is plastered on to the stone or brick, where it dries and hardens.

PACIFIC SWALLOW (*Hirundo tahitica*)        Plate 11A

**Layang-layang**

Length 5½ inches. Blue-black above, forehead, sides of head and throat chestnut, remaining underparts smoky grey. The tail is forked but the outer feathers do not extend far beyond the rest.

This is a common bird throughout the country at all elevations. It breeds from March to June on cliffs and in caves and also under bridges and on buildings, preferring unoccupied ones. The birds can often be seen at wet places and beside puddles collecting mud, and they line their nests with grass and feathers. There are usually three eggs, white, spotted with brown.

The BARN SWALLOW (*Hirundo rustica,* Fig. 5) breeds in northern Asia and is a winter visitor to our region. It can be distinguished from the resident species by the very deeply forked tail, the outer feathers of which are prolonged, and by the white (instead of smoky grey) belly. Between September and March these Swallows can be seen in large flocks and often roost in hundreds on telegraph wires.

Fig. 5.
Barn Swallow.

## CUCKOO-SHRIKES AND MINIVETS

This is not an easy group of birds to define collectively. All of them live mainly among the foliage of trees and feed on insects. The male and female plumage is usually different, and some species, especially the males, display brilliant colours.

PIED TRILLER (*Lalage nigra*)        Plate 11B

**Murai Batu**

Length 6½ inches. The male is black above with a band of white over each eye, wings black with conspicuous white bars, underparts entirely white. In the female the black is replaced by pale brown and the underparts are tinged with buff. This is a common bird in the lowlands and often seen in gardens, where it is sometimes confused with the far more abundant Magpie-Robin. If it is remembered that the latter bird has the throat and breast black and no white on the head this confusion need not arise.

The nest of the Pied Triller is placed in trees, usually at no great height on a horizontal fork. The eggs are dull green closely spotted with brown. Breeding season, February to August.

In the ASHY MINIVET (*Pericrocotus divaricatus,* Plate 12A) the upper parts are grey, head black in the male with a broad white band on the forehead, wings brown, underparts entirely white. The female is paler and lacks the black on the head. The more extensive white on the head and the absence of white bars on the wings are features which distinguish this Minivet from the Pied Triller, which it otherwise rather closely resembles. It is a winter visitor to our region and is seen most often in the lowlands near the coast.

MOUNTAIN MINIVET (*Pericrocotus solaris*)                    Plate 11c
**Burong Mata Hari**

Length 6½ inches. Male black and scarlet above, scarlet below except for the black throat; female similarly marked with black and bright yellow. The young males are yellow like the adult female. This is a mountain bird, common and conspicuous at the hill stations, where it can often be seen in small flocks along paths and in the jungle adjoining gardens. A nest has been recorded at Cameron Highlands, high up in a tree.

Two brightly coloured lowland Minivets can be mentioned. The SCARLET MINIVET (*Pericrocotus flammeus*) is found in foothill jungle and both sexes are indistinguishable in the field from the mountain species. However, as they never invade each others' territory there is no difficulty in identifying them.

The SMALL MINIVET (*Pericrocotus cinnamomeus,* Plate 11D) is a little smaller than the others and the male is similarly coloured, but the female has, in addition to her black and yellow livery, a patch of red above the tail. It is found on the coast and seems to have a preference for places where there are casuarina trees.

PLATE II. A. Pacific Swallow; B. Pied Triller; C. Mountain Minivet ♂, ♀; D. Small Minivet ♀.

A

B

C

D

INCHES

*Plate* 11

A

B

INCHES

C

D

*Plate* 12

# DRONGOS

The Drongos or King Crows are lively, attractive birds; all our species have black plumage glossed with metallic blue or green. They are tree-top dwellers, but make themselves conspicuous by flying out into the open in pursuit of winged insects. They are noisy and often mimic other birds, and they will usually defend the vicinity of their nests with great courage, even against human intruders. The nests are like little baskets or cradles slung below a forked twig of some lofty tree.

GREATER RACQUET-TAILED DRONGO (*Dicrurus paradiseus*)    Plate 12B
**Burong Chĕchawi**

Length 12 inches, not including the remarkable outer tail feathers, which may extend another 12 to 15 inches beyond this. The plumage is metallic black in both sexes, and the outer feathers of the tail on each side are greatly elongated in the form of a naked shaft with an oval 'racquet' of normal feather at the tip. When the bird is in flight the shafts are barely visible and one receives the impression of a black bird closely pursued by two large bees.

This Drongo is common in lowland and foothill country wherever there is any remnant of high jungle standing, as at Bukit Timah in Singapore. It makes a variety of curious noises among which are a loud, clear '*chee-yoop*' and a less melodious '*chee-chee-chee-kwa-kwa*' of which the Malay name is an abbreviated rendering. It also imitates other birds. The breeding habits are those of the family and the season extends from March to June. Three eggs are laid, pink with brown and purplish markings.

In the mountains its place is taken by a similar but slightly smaller bird, the LESSER RACQUET-TAILED DRONGO (*Dicrurus remifer*), **Chĕchawi Bukit**. In this species the racquets of the tail extend further along the shaft, rounded at the tip, tapering in the direction of the body.

Although it is a jungle bird the BRONZED DRONGO (*Dicrurus aeneus*) is seen fairly frequently at the hill stations and passes; it is not, however, by any means confined to the mountains. It is small, length 8½ inches, shining metallic black above and very dark grey on the belly. The tail is forked and turned outwards at the tip like a Y or a fish's tail.

PLATE 12.    A. Ashy Minivet; B. Greater Racquet-tailed Drongo; C. Black-naped Oriole, adult and young; D. Silver-eared Mesia.

# ORIOLES

These are brightly coloured birds, dwellers among the foliage of trees, nesting, like the Drongos, in a small fork high up and far out on the branch of a tree. They feed both on fruit and berries and on insects, especially caterpillars. Only one species is frequently seen in the Malay Peninsula.

BLACK-NAPED ORIOLE (*Oriolus chinensis*)                    Plate 12c
**Burong Kunyet Běsar**

Length 10½ inches. Male bright clear yellow with some black on the wings and tail and a black band encircling the crown of the head at the level of the eyes; female similar but less bright and tinged with green above. This is a rather local bird, but common and conspicuous where it occurs, and particularly common on Singapore Island, where it is very generally misnamed 'Golden Oriole', this being the correct name of a quite distinct species, not found in our region. This is one of the few birds which combines bright plumage with a pleasing voice; its call is a loud flute-like whistle, *'too-whee-you'*.

Although there is a breeding population in Singapore and at several places on the west coast, most of the Black-naped Orioles that we see are winter visitors, belonging to a subspecies indistinguishable in the field from the resident one. The nest is usually high up in a tree and very difficult of access. Two eggs are laid, bluish-white with purple-brown spots. Nests have been recorded in June.

# CROWS

In the Peninsula these birds are a much less general feature of the scenery than in European and continental Asian countries. Only one species can be said to be a common bird.

LARGE-BILLED CROW (*Corvus macrorhynchos*)                    Fig. 6
**Gagak, Děndang**

Length 19½ inches. Black all over glossed with green and purple, bill thick and powerful. Fairly common along the coast, especially

Fig. 6. Large-billed Crow.

around fishing villages, where it competes with the Kites in scavenging. It is often seen in flocks of twenty or more. The nest is usually built in a tall tree in mangrove. It is a bulky structure made of sticks and lined with grass and fibre. Three or four eggs are laid, light greenish spotted with brown and purple. Breeding season, January to June.

At Klang in Selangor there is a colony of HOUSE CROWS (*Corvus splendens*) which has its origin in the introduction, about 1895, of birds from Ceylon to combat a plague of caterpillars which were damaging the coffee plantations. The action of the planters in introducing this crow was most ill-considered, for the bird has recently increased in numbers and has become a pest in the area. Curiously enough it has not yet spread inland, but has remained confined to a small area along the coast. During the Japanese occupation another small colony was established, by some unknown agency, in the Tanjong Pagar area of Singapore. It is distinguished from the native species by the grey neck, upper back and breast; the rest of the plumage is glossy black.

### BABBLERS

This is an extremely diverse group of birds with no obvious character descriptive of all of them. We have nearly fifty species mostly small, obscure birds which lurk in thick undergrowth and are difficult to see and hard to identify when seen. Most of the exceptions to this rule are mountain birds, and a few species of Babblers are conspicuous at the hill stations.

SILVER-EARED MESIA (*Leiothrix argentauris*) Plate 12D

Length 7 inches. Olive-grey above, orange-yellow below, bright crimson patches on the wings and (in the male) at the base of the tail; head black with a silvery-white patch on each cheek. This pretty bird is very common at the hill stations and is usually seen in flocks of four or five to a dozen, hunting for insects among the bushes and undergrowth. It maintains a continuous chuckling and clucking and also has a clear whistling note which is most frequently heard in the early morning.

The nest is a deep cup built in a bush or in undergrowth, and two or three eggs are laid, white, sparsely spotted with brown. Breeding is mainly in February and March.

LONG-TAILED SIBIA (*Heterophasia picaoides*) Plate 13A

Length 13 inches of which over 9 inches is tail. Dark grey above, paler grey below with a conspicuous white spot on the wing. The feathers of the tail are progressively longer towards the middle, so that it appears stepped or graduated along its edges. This is another common and familiar hill-station bird. It is seen in small flocks, flying from tree to tree and climbing about among the foliage, and is tame and easily approached.

The nest is built out on the branches of high trees and is usually inaccessible; no doubt for this reason eggs have not been described from our region, though nests have been observed in March and April.

CHESTNUT-CAPPED LAUGHING THRUSH (*Garrulax mitratus*) Plate 13B

Length 9 inches. Bluish-grey above with a white bar on the wing, grey on the breast passing to chestnut-brown on the belly; top of head bright chestnut, a white ring round the eye; bill and feet yellow. This handsome Babbler is another mountain bird. It goes about in small flocks when feeding, but generally keeps to thick cover and is not

PLATE 13. A. Long-tailed Sibia; B. Chestnut-capped Laughing-Thrush; C. Golden Babbler; D. Striped Tit-Babbler; E. Common Iora.

42

INCHES

C

D

A

E

B

*Plate* 13

A

B

INCHES

C

D

*Plate* 14

very easy to see. Its song, however, is frequently heard, a rather loud '*kwo-kwee kwo-kwee*'. A nest has been recorded in April at Fraser's Hill, cup-shaped, made of roots and fibres, and containing one egg, deep blue without markings.

A curious phenomenon often encountered in hill jungle is the 'bird-wave'. Walking along a path you may find yourself suddenly surrounded by numbers of small birds of various kinds, flitting through the branches and undergrowth, perching, climbing and flitting on, all preserving the same general direction, so that in a minute or so they are gone. It appears that companies of insect-eating birds band together and work through an area of jungle. An insect accidentally disturbed by a single searching bird is likely to fly away and escape, but if a numerous company of them is present it may well alight within sight of a bird other than the one which disturbed it, and so be captured. The interesting feature of these waves is that various species of birds co-operate in them. Two kinds of Babblers are very frequently represented.

One of these is the MOUNTAIN FULVETTA (*Alcippe peracensis*), length 6 inches. This is a sober-coloured bird, smoky grey above and on the head, lighter grey below, wings and tail brown. A curved black stripe from over each eye to the sides of the neck is the only con-spicuous feature of the plumage; the legs are flesh-coloured.

The other frequent participant in the mountain bird-waves is the little GOLDEN BABBLER (*Stachyris chrysaea*, illustrated in Plate 13c), length 3½ inches. This is a tiny bird, greenish-yellow above, bright yellow below, with the forepart of the crown golden. Like many very small birds it is extremely tame and will sometimes allow approach within arm's length.

STRIPED TIT-BABBLER (*Macronus gularis*)                    Plate 13D

Length 4¼ inches. Chestnut above, darker on the head and wings, pale yellow below streaked with black on the throat and breast. This inconspicuous little bird is nevertheless the most frequently seen of the lowland Babblers, most of which very seldom venture out of dense jungle. It is widely distributed and specially common in sandy coastal districts on both sides of the country. It is sometimes seen in small flocks and constantly utters a low scolding note.

PLATE 14. A. Yellow-vented Bulbul; B. Yellow-crowned Bulbul; C. Black-headed Bulbul; D. Red-whiskered Bulbul.

The nest is usually low down in a bush, sometimes in quite open situations. It is made of bamboo leaves or grass and is globular in shape with the entrance at the side. Usually there are two eggs, white with brown spots. Breeding season, January to July.

## IORAS AND LEAFBIRDS

This is a small group of birds, nearly all of which have green or yellow plumage and live in the foliage of trees, often far above the ground. Their habits render them inconspicuous and only one species can be described as common.

COMMON IORA (*Aegithina tiphia*)                              Plate 13E
**Burong Kunyet Kĕchil**

Length 5¾ inches. The male is bright yellow below, greenish-yellow above with the tail and wings black, the latter with two white bars. The female is less bright and more greenish in colour. This is a common bird in open lowland country, especially in coastal areas where casuarina trees are plentiful. It generally stays fairly high up in the trees and its most usual call is a high-pitched, long-drawn '*zeeeeeee-yow*', the pitch falling abruptly with the terminal '*yow*'. It is easily mistaken for the call of a cicada.

The nest is a neat cup placed out on the branch of a tree, usually at a fair height above the ground. The normal complement of eggs is three, greenish-white with brown spots. Breeding season, April to July.

Of the LEAFBIRDS (genus *Chloropsis*), **Burong Daun**, there are several similar species, equally numerous though not very often seen, and they are best considered collectively. They are fairly small birds (length about 7 to 8 inches) and their plumage is mainly bright green, with a certain amount of blue and yellow; the males have a conspicuous black patch on the throat. Their colour blends with the leaves and makes them difficult to see, but a little time spent in watching the high jungle foliage with field-glasses will generally discover them. They frequently travel in small parties.

# BULBULS

This well-known group of birds is represented by nearly thirty species In the Peninsula. Most of them are rather drab coloured, and all but a few uncommon or difficult to distinguish from each other. They are fine, cheerful songsters and spend their time in trees and bushes, usually at no great height from the ground.

YELLOW-VENTED BULBUL (*Pycnonotus goiavier*)                Plate 14A
**Mĕrbah**

Length 7½ inches. Upper parts and tail dull brown, head dark brown on top with a white streak over each eye; underparts brownish-white with a patch of lemon-yellow under the tail. This is possibly our commonest bird in inhabited country, and is to be found in almost every garden. Anyone who wakes up a little before dawn and listens will hear first one and then another of these birds start to greet the day with its pleasant bubbling, galloping song. It is quite omnivorous, feeding on fruit and berries as well as insects of all kinds. It is really a bird of the lowlands, but has followed man into the mountains and is established in the inhabited parts of the hill stations.

The main breeding season is from February to June and nests are built usually in low bushes, often in bougainvillea bushes in gardens or in the hibiscus hedges that border them. The nest is a deep cup of grass and leaves lined with vegetable fibre, and two eggs are laid, pinkish-white closely speckled all over with reddish-brown and lavender.

YELLOW-CROWNED BULBUL (*Pycnonotus zeylanicus*)        Plate 14B
**Barau-barau**

Length 11 inches. Brown above tinged with greenish on the wings and tail, white and greyish below, buff under the tail; top of head golden yellow. This large Bulbul is a lowland bird, abundant along the courses of the larger rivers and fairly frequently seen and heard in gardens and cultivated land generally. The song is most delightful, a far louder, richer version of the bubbling dawn song of the Yellow-vented Bulbul.

The nest is a shallow cup of twigs and grass built at no great height in a tree in open scrub country. Two eggs are laid, white closely marked with reddish- and purplish-brown. Breeding season, March to June.

BLACK-HEADED BULBUL (*Pycnonotus atriceps*)      Plate 14C
**Burong Siam**

Length 7 inches. Olive-yellow above and below, brighter over and under the tail, which is tipped with yellow; wings edged with black, head and neck glossy black. This is a very handsome bird, found in the lowlands and foothills throughout the country, but more common in the north. It frequents dry secondary jungle, and is less a bird of inhabited country than the two Bulbuls already described. The nests are found, sometimes several close together, in small trees and bushes, and the eggs are pale pink rather sparsely spotted with reddish-brown. Breeding season, March to May.

RED-WHISKERED BULBUL (*Pycnonotus jocosus*)      Plate 14D
**Měrbah Jambul**

Length 8 inches. Greyish-brown above and white below except for a patch of bright crimson under the tail; a conspicuous black crest on the head, cheeks white with a small crimson patch. This dandy among the Bulbuls is really a bird of continental Asia, and is very common in Thailand. It extends into Malaysia about as far south as the latitude of Penang and is a familiar garden bird in Perlis, Kedah and northern Kelantan. It is occasionally seen farther south as it is a favourite cage-bird, and escaped birds may establish themselves far from their main wild population.

## THRUSHES AND ROBINS

In our region this well-known group of birds is not very well represented but there are a few familiar and conspicuous species. The Nightingale is a kind of Thrush, and all over the world Thrushes are renowned as song-birds; we have two common species which well sustain this reputation.

PLATE 15. A. Magpie-Robin; B. White-rumped Shama ♂, ♀; C. Chestnut-naped Forktail; D. Common Tailorbird.

INCHES

A

B

C

D

Plate 15

B

A

C

INCHES

*Plate* 16

MAGPIE-ROBIN (*Copsychus saularis*) Plate 15A
**Murai**

Length 8½ inches. Head, neck, throat and breast and all the upper parts black, underparts behind the breast white, a bar on the wing and the outer tail feathers white. Reference has been made to the similarity of this bird to the Pied Triller (p. 38), which is distinguished by having more white in the plumage and no black on the underparts. The female Magpie-Robin is dull grey where the male is black. This bird may be said to share with the Yellow-vented Bulbul the distinction of being our commonest garden bird, and its conspicuous pied plumage makes it perhaps even more familiar. Like that species it has followed man up into the hill stations. It feeds on worms and insects and spends a great deal of time in the open on lawns and flower-beds searching for them.

Its song is a loud, clear whistle, produced in a great variety of phrases, and the males often quarrel to the accompaniment of a harsh scolding noise. The nest is seldom far from the ground, banks and hollow tree stumps being frequently chosen as sites for it, and it is sometimes built in abandoned buildings and other artificial structures. It is a fairly large, shallow cup, and the eggs, usually three, are greenish thickly marked with brown and purple. Breeding season, January to June.

WHITE-RUMPED SHAMA (*Copsychus malabaricus*) Plate 15B
**Murai Hutan, Murai Batu**

Length 10½ inches, of which, in the male, 7 inches is tail. Head, breast and upper parts black, hinder part of back and edges of tail white, underparts behind the breast chestnut. The female is duller than the male and her tail is shorter by about two inches. The Shama is quite a common bird, but far less often seen than the Magpie Robin, as it seldom ventures into the open. Its haunts are in thick secondary jungle in the lowlands, such as that which borders on rubber estates and small country villages. It is not shy of human habitations, however, and its song can often be heard from the gardens of houses in country districts, if there is thick cover near by.

This is our finest song-bird. The song is much like that of the

PLATE 16. A. Yellow-bellied Prinia; B. Fan-tailed Cisticola; C. Pied Fantail; D. Great Niltava ♂, ♀.

47

Magpie-Robin, but more melodious in tone and even more varied. The nest and eggs are almost indistinguishable from those of the other species.

CHESTNUT-NAPED FORKTAIL (*Enicurus ruficapillus*) Plate 15c
**Burong Chĕgar**

Length 8 inches. Top of head and neck rich chestnut, back black behind the neck, white over the tail, wings and tail black and white; underparts white marked with black on the breast. The chestnut extends further back from the head in the female. The tail in both sexes is long and deeply forked.

This beautiful bird is quite confined to torrential streams in the foothills and mountains below 3,000 feet. It can be seen, usually in pairs, among the rocks and boulders in these streams, but the casual observer is likely to meet with it only where they intersect a road or path, as walking in or beside them is usually rather difficult going. When disturbed the birds fly a short distance along the stream, uttering a high, clear whistle. The nest is made of moss and built on a ledge of rock beside a stream. Two eggs are laid, pure white spotted with brown and lavender at the larger end.

Although not nearly so numerous, the SLATY-BACKED FORKTAIL (*Enicurus schistaceus*) is possibly more familiar as it is common along the mountain streams at Cameron Highlands, which are extensively accessible to comfortable walking. It is larger than the species last described (length 10 inches) and differs chiefly in having no chestnut in the plumage, the upper parts being black and dark grey. It is quite confined to mountain torrents above 3,000 feet, where it takes the place of the Chestnut-naped Forktail, and its habits are very simliar.


TAILORBIRDS AND WARBLERS

These are all small, slender birds with sober brown or greenish plumage and strictly insectivorous habits. Many of them are noisy little birds, more often heard than seen, and are often recognizable by a distinctive song. Some of the Warblers of temperate regions are beautiful songsters, but none of the species resident in the Peninsula excel in this respect. About twenty species have been recorded from this country, half of which are winter visitors which breed far to the north. None of these is very common and all the Warblers described here are resident. Very few of the species are distinguished by Malay names, but the collective term **Laki Padi** is applied to most of them.

COMMON TAILORBIRD (*Orthotomus sutorius*)　　　　　　　　Plate 15D

Length 5½ inches. Upper parts olive-green with a white edge to the wing, underparts whitish; top of head orange-chestnut, sides of face streaked black and white. This little bird is very common in the low-lands wherever there is fairly thick cover close to the ground. Over-grown hedges, unweeded rubber estates and the less tidy parts of gardens are all favourite habitats. It is far more often heard than seen, its call being a shrill, strident note of two syllables, repeated with monotonous regularity, '*chee-whit, chee-whit, chee-whit*', thirty to sixty or even well over a hundred times. It is particularly noisy in the nesting season.

The nest, which is similar in all the lowland Tailorbirds, is a very remarkable structure. Most usually a single large, living leaf is curled round by twisting strands of spider's web silk right round it, so that the opposite edges come together. These are then joined by a method usually described as sewing, but really more like riveting. Holes are punched opposite each other near the two edges, and tangled spider's web or tree-cotton (kapok) is pushed through and teased out on each side so as to hold the edges together. Sometimes two or three leaves are joined in this way. In the resultant pouch the nest is built of vegetable fibre mixed with tree-cotton or lalang down, and firmly anchored by stitches or rivets pierced through the leaf. It is usually not more than two or three feet from the ground. The eggs are pale blue, spotted around the larger end with reddish-brown. Breeding season about January to June.

The BLACK-NECKED TAILORBIRD (*Orthotomus atrogularis*) is distinguished by having the sides of the head grey, the edge of the wing yellow and (in males only) the throat black. Its call is just as strident and monotonous as that of the Common Tailorbird, but

49

is monosyllabic, '*zee, zee, zee, zee*'. The habits of the two species are similar and they are almost equally common.

In and near mangrove swamp a third species of Tailorbird is common, the ASHY TAILORBIRD (*Orthotomus ruficeps*). This species is ashy grey above, light grey to white below, and has, instead of just a chestnut cap, the greater part of the head and throat of this colour.

YELLOW-BELLIED PRINIA (*Prinia flaviventris*)      Plate 16A

Length 5¾ inches. Olive-brown above, top of head dark grey, tail long, brown tipped with white. Underparts white on the breast, yellow further back. This is a bird of grassland, particularly open country covered with lalang. It is most often seen in such situations, sitting on a bush or tall grass stem, singing a thin, shrill little song. The nest is a ball of grass with a hole in the side built a little above the ground in a clump of grass. The eggs are very beautiful, glossy bright chestnut with a band or cap of richer colour at the larger end. Breeding season, January to July and August.

FAN-TAILED CISTICOLA (*Cisticola juncidis*)      Plate 16B
**Burong Main Angin**

Length 4½ inches. Dull brown above streaked with black and lighter brown, paler over the tail, which is tipped with white; whitish washed with buff below. This is a common bird in open grassland, but is only conspicuous during the breeding season, when the males frequently fly jerkily up into the air calling '*tik, tik, tik*', and then dive steeply back again. The nest is a deep cup built of grass among long grass stems, close to the ground, and is very difficult to find. The eggs are greenish-white closely spotted with brown and grey. Breeding season, January to June.


## FLYCATCHERS

These are small insectivorous birds whose only obvious common character is their habit of flying out from a perch in a tree to catch winged insects and returning to it quickly after each excursion. In some of them the males are conspicuously coloured, often patterned with blue, sometimes with black and white, and in such cases they usually differ very markedly from the females. Over thirty species of Flycatchers have been recorded from the Malay Peninsula.

PIED FANTAIL (*Rhipidura javanica*)          Plate 16c
**Murai Gila**

Length 7 inches of which $3\frac{1}{2}$ inches is tail. Dark brown above with a white streak over the eye and all the tail feathers except the centre ones broadly tipped with white; underparts white, tinged with buff towards the tail and with a black band across the breast. This is a common bird in open country in the lowlands, especially near water, and is remarkable for its restless activity, constantly hopping and fluttering among the bushes and on the ground below them, posturing and opening and shutting the tail like a fan. It is this habit that has earned it its Malay name, 'Mad Robin'.

The nest is built a few feet from the ground in a bush or among bamboo and consists of a neat cup made of vegetable fibre. Two eggs are laid, yellowish-white with small brown spots, which often form a ring round the larger end. Breeding season, February to July.

In the hill stations the WHITE-THROATED FANTAIL (*Rhipidura albicollis*) can often be seen taking an active part in 'bird-waves' (p. 43). It is similar to the lowland species, but the whole of the underparts, except for the white throat, are dark grey.

BLACK-NAPED MONARCH (*Hypothymis azurea*)       Plate 17A
**Kělichap Ranting**

Length 6 inches. In the male the body is purplish-blue above and below, grading to white on the belly, the head and throat bright blue marked with black on the forehead and nape, and a black band on the throat. The female is bright blue only on the head, the remaining upper parts being greyish-brown, the throat purplish-blue passing through grey to white on the belly. This Flycatcher is common in scrub and open wooded country in the lowlands and foothills, and in the winter months can sometimes be seen in small flocks. The nest is a deep cup of moss and fibre, usually in a tree at no great height, and two eggs are laid, pinkish-white with brown spots. Breeding season, April to July.

There is a great variety (about seventeen species) of these Blue Flycatchers in the Peninsula. One other species can be mentioned, the MANGROVE BLUE FLYCATCHER (*Muscicapa rufigastra*). Here the sexes are alike, the upper parts being dark blue and the underparts orange. This bird is strictly confined to mangrove, but in this habitat it is quite common.

ASIAN PARADISE FLYCATCHER (*Terpsiphone paradisi*)
**Murai Ekor Gading**

Length of female 7 to 8 inches. The male is found in two plumage phases, a case of dimorphism recalling those of the Reef Egret and the Changeable Hawk-Eagle, except that here it is confined to the one sex. It may be chestnut above and on the tail, the head black and the underparts grey, grading to white on the belly, or the whole of the plumage may be pure white except for the black head. In both phases the central tail feathers, chestnut or white, are prolonged into two ribbon-like streamers, which may be as much as 16 inches long. In the white phase this is one of our most striking and ornamental birds. The female is similar to the brown male, but has a tail of normal length.

This Flycatcher is not uncommon in the lowlands and foothills, but is mainly a jungle bird and does not frequent inhabited country. It is most often seen flying across the road where it runs through jungle, and the male, with its long streamers fluttering behind it, is quite unmistakable. It builds a typical Flycatcher type of nest, a deep cup placed in a fork of a small tree, and lays three eggs, white spotted with reddish-brown.

GREAT NILTAVA (*Muscicapa grandis*)                    Plate 16D

Length 8 inches. Male, except for the black wings and forehead, dark, shining blue all over; female brown, bluish-grey on the top of the head, with a light blue spot on each side of the neck. This is a mountain bird and common at the hill stations, where it can often be seen on jungle paths, on or near the ground, or hawking insects in clearings. Its call is a soft musical whistle of three ascending notes.

It has the unusual habit of building either a domed or a cup-shaped nest. Two eggs are laid, pale pink, tinged with buff, speckled all over with darker buff. Breeding season, February to June.

Another common mountain species is the LITTLE PIED FLYCATCHER (*Muscicapa westermanni*), length 4 inches. The male is entirely black above with a long white streak over the eye and a white bar on the wing, pure white below. The female is very different, brown and grey above, greyish-white below. This little bird is another regular participant in 'bird-waves' (p. 43) and is also often seen in pairs, when the obscurely coloured female can easily be identified by association with the quite unmistakable male.


## WAGTAILS AND PIPITS

These are small birds, most of which spend their time on or near the ground in open situations. A distinctive feature of them is that they progress by running instead of hopping, as do most birds of this size and general aspect. The Wagtails are all winter visitors to our region, and we have only one common Pipit.

GREY WAGTAIL (*Motacilla cinerea*)          Plate 17B
**Pipit Batu, Kědidi**

Length 8 inches of which over 3 inches is tail. Upper parts brownish-grey with a greenish-yellow patch over the tail, wings black marked with white, tail black edged with white; white below grading to yellow on the belly. This is the winter plumage; just before leaving us in the spring for their northern breeding grounds these Wagtails, especially the males, become brighter. A triangular black patch develops on the throat and the upper parts change to clear grey. From August to April this is a common bird, both in the lowlands and the mountains, and often seen along the hill roads and streams. When running on the ground it constantly wags its tail up and down, and in flight, which is dipping or undulating, it calls, '*chisik, chisik*'. It feeds entirely on insects and catches much of its food in shallow water at the edges of streams.

RICHARD'S PIPIT (*Anthus novaeseelandiae*)   Plate 17c
**Pipit Padang, Chiak Padang, Chiak Tanah**

Length 6½ inches. Brown above mottled and streaked with black, tail darker, some white on the wings which shows only in flight; underparts light brown streaked with darker brown on the breast; legs pinkish. This is a very common bird, abundant in all kinds of dry grassy country, golf-courses, grazing grounds and the sides of roads, and is quite often seen on garden lawns. It spends most of its time running about on the ground, but quite often makes short soaring flights, when it calls '*chisik*', rather like a Wagtail.

The nest is made in grass on the ground, often on a sloping bank, and consists of a shallow cup built of dead grass. Three eggs are laid, white, so thickly mottled and spotted with dark brown that little of the ground colour is visible.

## STARLINGS AND MYNAS

These are all lowland birds of dark coloured plumage, having the common character that their gait is a walk; most other families of birds of similar size and general aspect progress by hopping. They are omnivorous and so very easy to feed; this fact, together with the capacity of some of them for mimicking various sounds, including even human speech, makes them favourites as pets and cage-birds.

PHILIPPINE GLOSSY STARLING (*Aplonis panayensis*)   Plate 18A
**Pĕrling**

Length 8¼ inches. Adults are easily recognized, being very dark glossy green all over with the eye bright red. Immature birds are very different, brown above, whitish below, heavily streaked with black. This is a common and familiar bird in towns, but in the countryside is rather irregularly distributed and confined to the lowlands. It feeds mainly on fruit of various kinds and seldom comes down to the ground. Breeding is mainly from about March to June but continues throughout the year. In the country the nest is built in holes in trees but in towns it is often made under the eaves of buildings. Three eggs are laid, blue spotted with dark brown.

PLATE 17. A. Black-naped Monarch ♂, ♀; B. Grey Wagtail; C. Richard's Pipit; D. Little Spiderhunter.

A

D

INCHES

B

C

*Plate* 17

C

A

INCHES

D

Plate 18

The very large flocks of Starlings which occur in the lowlands in the winter months are not composed of this species, but of the DAURIAN STARLING (*Sturnus sturninus*). The adult is glossy black above with a white bar on the wing, the head and breast grey, the remaining underparts whitish. Many of the birds in these flocks are immature and grey where the adults are black. This bird is a winter visitor and is seen in our region from about October to March.

HILL MYNA or TIONG (*Gracula religiosa*)                     Plate 18B
**Burong Tiong**

Length 12 inches. Glossy black everywhere except for a white patch on the wing, conspicuous when the bird flies. The bill, feet, a patch of skin below the eye and a fleshy wattle behind it, are yellow. This bird does not frequent towns and inhabited areas like the other Starlings and Mynas, but prefers open country with tall trees, especially when these include dead trees; in such situations it is quite common. Like the Philippine Glossy Starling (but unlike the other Mynas) it does not come down to the ground.

The most usual call is the loud, clear whistle which has given it its Malay name, but it often mimics other birds and, in captivity, can be taught to imitate the human voice. Of all our Starlings it is the most valued as a cage-bird. Nests are made in holes in trees, often dead ones, high up and difficult of access. The two or three eggs are greenish-blue blotched with brown. Main breeding season, February to May.

COMMON MYNA (*Acridotheres tristis*)                     Plate 18C
**Gĕmbala**

Length 9¾ inches. Purplish-brown above with a white patch on each wing, conspicuous in flight, head and breast black, paling through brown to white under the tail, which is black tipped with white; bill, feet and a patch of skin round and behind the eye yellow. This is now a very common bird in the Peninsula, but thirty years ago it was known only in the extreme north. Since then it has advanced down the Peninsula and seems to be replacing the indigenous and very similar Jungle Myna. The Common Myna is the species most often seen in gardens and open spaces in towns, stalking about on the grass with an air of great self-assurance, or

PLATE 18. A. Philippine Glossy Starling; B. Hill Myna; C. Common Myna; D Java Sparrow

5                                55

flying among the trees and bushes in small flocks. Together with the Jungle Myna they seek the company of buffaloes and cattle and often perch on the animals' backs. They may sometimes pick ticks off them, but their main interest, like that of the Cattle Egrets (p. 10), is in the insects which are disturbed by the beasts' trampling.

The song is a curious medley of whistling, squeaking and chattering, '*quee-quee-quee, churr-churr-churr, kok-kok-kok*', etc, etc., and sometimes a harsh screech when the bird is frightened or disturbed. They nest under the eaves and in other convenient situations in houses, and in holes in trees, the nest itself being an untidy affair of twigs, grass, bits of paper, etc. The eggs are greenish-blue without spots. Breeding goes on throughout the year but is mainly from February to May.

The JUNGLE MYNA (*Acridotheres fuscus*), **Gĕmbala Kĕrbau**, to which reference has already been made, is very similar but a little smaller, greyish-brown where the Common Myna is purplish, and lacks the yellow patch of skin round the eye. This bird is a native of our region, and although it appears to be giving ground before the invading Common Myna, is still very common. The habits of the two species are practically the same.


### SUNBIRDS AND SPIDERHUNTERS

This is a very distinctive group of birds, small to very small in size, with the bill long, slender and curved downwards. They feed partly on insects and partly on nectar which they collect from flowers just as bees do, often puncturing the base of the flower to get at it. The Spiderhunters probably eat a larger proportion of insects and spiders than do the Sunbirds. The latter are all small or tiny birds in which the males are variously and often brilliantly coloured and the females almost uniformly olive-green above and yellow below. It follows that while male Sunbirds are easy to identify, it is very hard to distinguish the females of the different species.

Sunbirds are sometimes confused with Humming-Birds, with which they share the characters of small size and brilliant plumage and of feeding on nectar. Humming-Birds, however, are really quite distinct and are entirely confined to the American continents.

YELLOW-BREASTED SUNBIRD (*Nectarinia jugularis*)      Plate 19A
**Kĕlichap**

Length 4½ inches. Both sexes are olive-green above and yellow below, and the male has the forehead, throat and upper breast metallic blue-black. This is probably our commonest Sunbird in the lowlands, especially near the coast, and is frequently seen in gardens. The call, which is almost always uttered when the bird takes to flight, is a very shrill *'chip, chip, chip'*, sounding rather like two pebbles being knocked together.

The nest consists of a little flask-shaped purse built hanging from a twig, or frequently from a telephone wire or any permanently undisturbed structure of wire or rope about a house, such as the cord of a disused sunblind. It is made of vegetable fibre, moss, spider's web, etc., and lined with tree-cotton or lalang down. The entrance hole is rather above the middle, and there is invariably a little projecting eave just over it and an untidy, ragged 'tail' of scraps of leaf hanging from the lower end of the nest. Two eggs are laid, greenish-white with dark brown spots and lines. Breeding season, December to May.

BROWN-THROATED SUNBIRD (*Anthreptes malacensis*)      Plate 19B
**Kĕlichap Mayang Kĕlapa**

Length 5½ inches. The male has the head, neck and forepart of the back dark metallic green, the hinder part of the back metallic purple and the wings brown. The throat is pale brown bordered by a moustache-like streak of metallic purple, the remaining underparts yellow. The female has the usual olive-green and yellow plumage. Considerably larger than the last species, this is also a common Sunbird in the lowlands, occurring in kampongs and gardens, especially where there are coconut trees. They feed largely on the nectar of the palm flowers and on the insects which frequent them.

The nest is built in the same way as that of the Yellow-breasted Sunbird and hung up in a tree or bush. It is more pear-shaped and less elongate and appears more tidy than the other; the eave over the entrance is always present and there is usually a 'tail' of scraps hanging from the lower end. The two eggs are white marked with blotches and irregular lines of purple and purplish-brown. Breeding season, January to July.

The most brilliant of our species is the YELLOW-BACKED or CRIMSON SUNBIRD (*Aethopyga siparaja*, Plate 19C). The male has the head and whole front half of the body, above and below, bright crimson. The hinder back is yellow and the belly grey and there is a metallic purple stripe on each side of the throat, below the eye; the tail is also metallic purple. This is a local bird, occurring in scrub-jungle near the coast. It is mentioned both on account of its remarkable beauty and because it is rather common on Singapore Island, sometimes coming into gardens. The female is just like any other female Sunbird.

BLACK-THROATED SUNBIRD (*Aethopyga saturata*)

Length 5½ inches. The male has most of the plumage dark metallic violet, crimson and black with the lower breast yellow and the belly grey. The female is of the usual Sunbird pattern but has a yellow band above the tail. This species is very common in the mountains and, being extremely tame and much addicted to feeding from flowers, is often seen in the hill-station gardens. It will even come into verandas if there are potted plants flowering in them. Nests have been recorded, attached to the tips of the fronds of tree-ferns, in the early months of the year. The eggs are white streaked and spotted with brown.

LITTLE SPIDERHUNTER (*Arachnothera longirostra*)          Plate 17D
**Kělichap Jantong Pisang**

Length 6½ inches, of which the bill accounts for 1½. Olive-green above, the tail brown tipped with white; underparts mainly yellow, grey on the throat and upper breast, a tuft of brighter yellow feathers on either side of the breast in the male. Both sexes look rather like a large, very long-billed female Sunbird. This is mainly a lowland bird and is common in thick secondary jungle and in gardens and estates bordering on this kind of country. It is particularly attached to wild banana plants and obtains its food, the usual combination of nectar and insects, from them and various other flowers. The flight is very swift and well controlled, so that the bird can fly at high speed through thick cover. In flight it calls, like the Sunbirds, a sharp '*chik, chik*'.

The nest of this (and other Spiderhunters) is very curious. The bird seeks out a large, horizontally disposed leaf, often a banana leaf, and attaches to its under-surface a long tube or trough of fibre, moss and leaves. This is done by a sewing or riveting technique exactly like that of the Tailorbirds. The Spiderhunter punches a large number of holes through the leaf and threads spider's web through them, teasing it into a knot on the outside of the leaf and tangling it into the fabric of the nest below. The end of the tube facing inwards, towards the trunk, is left open as an entrance, the other end is closed and contains the egg chamber. The wonderfully accurate flight of these birds is well shown when they enter the nest. The bird simply flies straight in like a bullet, closing its wings at the last moment (this observation was made on another species, the Long-billed Spiderhunter, but no doubt applies to all of them). Two eggs are laid, white with a zone of purplish-brown spots round the larger end. Breeding season, December to March.

In the mountains the STREAKED SPIDERHUNTER (*Arachnothera magna*) is common and quite often comes into gardens in the hill stations. It is olive above, yellow below and heavily streaked with black all over. There is a black bar near the end of the tail, and it differs from all other Spiderhunters in having the feet bright orange. It has the same partiality for banana plants as the last species.


## FLOWERPECKERS

These tiny, usually brilliant birds are dwellers among the foliage of trees and spend much of their time high up and out of sight, but when they do descend to lower levels they attract attention by their bright colours. These are not metallic (as in the Sunbirds) and, when present, are always some shade of yellow, orange or red. Flower-peckers also differ from Sunbirds in having the bill quite short and in being even smaller; the smallest species measure less than three inches. They feed on insects and small fruits and berries, and their call is a sharp clicking sound. One Malay name, **Sĕpah Putri**, covers all of them.

SCARLET-BACKED FLOWERPECKER (*Dicaeum cruentatum*)    Plate 19D
Length 3½ inches. The male has the top of the head and the whole of the back bright scarlet, the wings, tail and sides of the head black,

and the underparts white darkening to grey on the sides. In the female the upper parts are olive-brown except for a scarlet patch over the tail. This is a common bird in the lowlands in open scrub country, especially near the coast. It feeds on insects and berries and is particularly fond of the sticky fruit of a parasitic mistletoe-like plant (*Loranthus*) that infests rubber and fruit trees. It probably plays a part in spreading this plant by getting seeds stuck to its bill when feeding, and then wiping them off on a branch of another tree.

The nest is a very neat little purse-like structure made mainly of vegetable down, such as kapok, and attached to a twig at a point well covered with leaves. Up to four eggs are laid, dull white in colour. Breeding season, January to July.

ORANGE-BELLIED FLOWERPECKER (*Dicaeum trigonostigma*)    Plate 19E

Length 3½ inches. The male is orange on the back and belly, the wings and head dark grey, the throat and breast pale grey. The female is greenish-yellow where her mate is orange, olive-green to grey elsewhere. Quite as common as the last species, this Flowerpecker has a wider range, ascending into the foothills and also entering gardens and even towns, more frequently. Its habits, nest and eggs are very much like those of the Scarlet-backed Flowerpecker.


## WHITE-EYES

These are very small birds, rather like some of the Warblers to look at, always yellowish-green with a ring of white feathers round the eye. Only one species is common in the Peninsula.

ORIENTAL WHITE-EYE (*Zosterops palpebrosa*)
**Kĕlichap Kunyet**

Length 4 inches. Greenish-yellow above, yellow and pale grey below, the white ring round the eye conspicuous, tail blackish. Fairly common near the coast, especially in mangrove or casuarina trees. The birds feed in small parties during the day on insects, and collect into large flocks in the evening. The nest is a neat but rather unsubstantial little cup slung from a forked twig; usually two eggs are laid, pale blue in colour. The breeding season is long, extending from December to August and possibly beyond these limits.


## SPARROWS AND MUNIAS

These are all small birds, rather dumpy and thick-set in appearance and having as a common character a very thick, strong bill, which is used for crushing the seeds on which they feed. There are three very distinct common species (though one of them is not a native of our region) and several species of the little birds called Munias, which can easily be recognized collectively by their habits. They feed in small flocks on the ground in grassy places, eating the grass seeds. The flock constantly moves forward by the hindmost birds flying a few yards and settling in front of the foremost. Not infrequently the flocks contain Munias of more than one species.

In some places these birds, and also the Baya Weaver, are a serious pest in rice-fields when the grain is ripening. At this time small shelters in the fields are manned by children and by the aged, who work some bird-scaring device, jerking a cord which causes clappers or tin-cans to bang together.

WHITE-HEADED MUNIA (*Lonchura maja*)　　　　　　Plate 20A
**Pipit Uban**

Length 4 inches. This is the most easily recognized of the Munias, chestnut-brown, blackish on the belly, with the whole head and neck white, a colour scheme that has earned for it the alternative name of Cigar Bird. It is very common in the lowlands in grasslands and paddy-fields, and has the habits described above for the genus. The nest is an untidy ball of grass, usually placed in a bush not far from the ground. The eggs, four or five in number, are pure white. Breeding continues throughout most of the year.

The CHESTNUT MUNIA (*Lonchura malacca*), **Pipit Merah**, is very similar, but has the head and neck black instead of white and the underparts rather richer brown. It is fairly common in the lowlands.

Spotted Munia (*Lonchura punctulata*)                    Plate 20B

Length 4 inches. Cinnamon-brown above barred with darker brown over the tail, the face chin and throat dark chocolate-brown; underparts whitish, each feather tipped with brown giving an effect of regular spots or scale-like markings. This is the species most often seen in gardens and grassy areas by roadsides. The nest is built high up in the crowns of palms and the birds can often be seen flying up to them trailing long strands of grass to be used as nesting material.

Rather less common than any of the above is the White-rumped Munia (*Lonchura striata*), **Pipit Dusun**, which is mostly dark brown above and greyish-white below, but distinguished by a conspicuous white patch on the back over the tail. It is fairly frequent in open country in the lowlands, and is of interest in being the only Munia that has followed man up to the hill stations.

Tree Sparrow (*Passer montanus*)                    Plate 20C
**Chiak Rumah, Pipit Rumah**

Length 5¼ inches. The Sparrow is so familiar that there is really no need to describe it. It lives only in the vicinity of towns and villages with permanent buildings, and is not found among the bamboo and attap-thatched houses of the kampongs. It seems doubtful whether it existed in the country at the not very remote period when these were the only human dwellings. It lives on grass seeds and scraps of food found around houses, and does not wait to be invited to share their meals with domestic chickens. The nest is an untidy mass of grass, feathers and other rubbish, usually constructed under the eaves of buildings or, if the birds are not sternly discouraged, in any convenient nook or ledge inside the house. Breeding goes on throughout the year but is more intense in the earlier months. The eggs are whitish thickly spotted and speckled with dark grey and brown.

The name Tree Sparrow certainly does not describe the bird's habits in eastern Asia, and has its origin in the circumstance that there is a subspecies of *Passer montanus* in Europe. There, however, it is not the Sparrow that is closely associated with man and his buildings, this being a distinct species, *Passer domesticus*, the House Sparrow, which is not found in our region. The habits of the European *montanus* are

PLATE 19. A. Yellow-breasted Sunbird ♂, ♀; B. Brown-throated Sunbird; C. Crimson Sunbird; D. Scarlet-backed Flowerpecker ♂, ♀; E. Orange-bellied Flowerpecker.

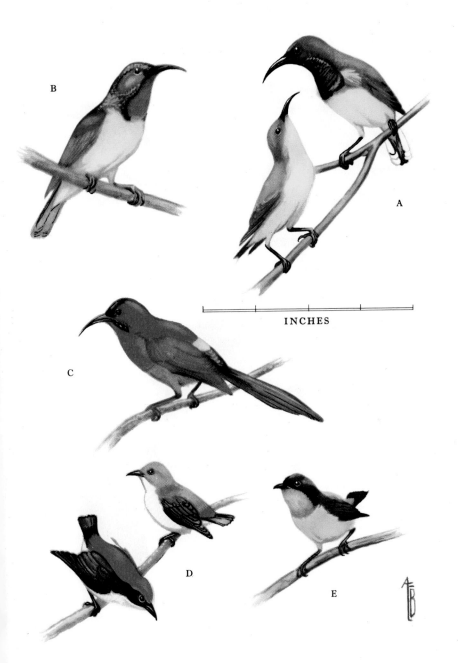

B

A

INCHES

C

D

E

*Plate* 19

C

B

D

INCHES

A

*Plate* 20

quite different from those of our Sparrow, it lives in open country and nests in trees. For this reason its English name is Tree Sparrow, and this name must be used for the species wherever it occurs and whatever its habits. An important difference between the two is that in the House Sparrow the sexes are very distinct whereas in the Tree Sparrow they are alike.

JAVA SPARROW (*Padda oryzivora*)                    Plate 18D
**Burong Jĕlatek**

Length 5½ inches. Upper parts and breast pale grey, belly pinkish, top of head, throat and tail black; a large white patch on each cheek, bill and feet pink. This handsome little bird is a native of Java and Sumatra and owes its existence as a wild species in the Peninsula to the fact that it is a favourite cage-bird and often escapes or is released. It is only found near human dwellings and is most common in the larger towns. Its nesting habits are similar to those of the Tree Sparrow and the eggs are white.

BAYA WEAVER (*Ploceus philippinus*)          Plate 20D; Fig. 7
**Burong Tĕmpua**

Length 6 inches. Light brown with darker streaks above, buff below passing to white on the belly. This description applies to both sexes outside the breeding season; during this period, about December to March, the adult male is bright yellow on the crown and black on the throat and sides of the head. This bird is common in open country in the lowlands, where it occurs in quite large flocks which fly in close formation, turning in unison just as flocks of Starlings do.

They make their nests in colonies in trees standing in open country. The nest is a most remarkable structure, built entirely of grass woven tightly together, flask-shaped, rounded at the bottom, tapering up to the point where it is suspended from a branch. At one side, near the bottom, a tubular entrance hangs down, its lower end finished off with a lace-like fringe. The material for the nest consists of strips of grass which the bird obtains by cutting a notch in the grass-blade and tearing off a strip a foot or two in length; no stalks or entire blades are used. Almost all the nest-building is done by the

PLATE 20.  A. White-headed Munia; B. Spotted Munia; C. Tree Sparrow; D. Baya Weaver ♂, ♀.

63

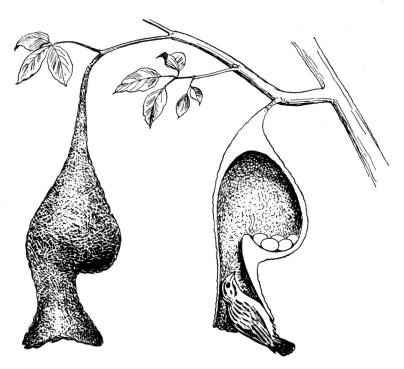

Fig. 7. Nests of the Baya Weaver that on the right shown in section.

male, who is joined by a female when it is nearing completion. Half-finished nests are often found in the colonies, presumably the work of males discouraged by lack of a partner. These are like the upper part of an entire nest, but the cavity is left open in a downward direction, with a bar or stirrup built across it. It has been observed that the nests are usually built in trees infested by the Red Tree Ant or Kĕrengga, an arrangement which certainly works to the disadvantage of anyone who tries to climb up to them. Usually three eggs are laid, white without markings.

# INDEX

ENGLISH NAMES *are in ordinary type*
MALAY NAMES *are in bold type*
LATIN NAMES *are in italic type*
FAMILIES *are in small capitals*